Mental M Practice 6

C000010999

Peter Clarke

Christina Rossiter

Heinemann Educational Publishers
Halley Court, Jordan Hill, Oxford OX2 8EJ
a division of Reed Educational & Professional Publishing Ltd

Oxford Melbourne Auckland
Florence Prague Madrid Athens
Singapore Tokyo Sao Paulo
Chicago Portsmouth NH (USA) Mexico City
Ibadan Gaborone Johannesburg
Kampala Nairobi Kuala Lumpur

First published 1997

00 99 98
10 9 8 7 6 5 4 3 2

ISBN 0435 02414 0
pack of 8: 0435 02420 5
teachers book: 0435 02421 3

Designed by Artistix
Typeset and illustrated by TechType, Abingdon, Oxon.
Cover design by Peter Campbell
Printed and bound by Scotprint

Exercise 1

A

1. $9 \times 8 =$

2. 4569, ☐, 4571, 4572

3. $23 + 23 + 12 =$ *58*

4. $265 + 423 =$

5. $12 \times 6 =$

6. $48 - ☐ = 25$ *23*

7. $16 \div 4 =$

8. $\frac{1}{2} + \frac{1}{4} =$

9. $3^2 =$

10. 3285, 3295, ☐ *3305*, 3315

11. $-5 + 7 =$ *2*

12. $\frac{1}{4} = 0\cdot☐ = ☐\%$

13. $(5 \times 4) - 6 =$

14. $85 \div 5 =$ *17*

15. 25% of 120 =

Copy and complete.

+	32		16	
	49			
23		52		
45				99
		44		

B

1. Write 10 201 in words.

2. Round 1785 to the nearest 1000.

3. What value has the 5 in 15 217?

4. Is the answer to $767 + 426$ nearer 1100 or 1200?

5. Give 2 factors of 24.

6. Simon builds a house using 36 cubes. 25% are red. How many is this?

7. Name a prime number between 1 and 5.

8. $4^2 + 3 =$

9. Sandra read 216 pages of her book last week and 385 pages this week. How many pages has she read altogether?

10. Chocolate biscuits come in packets of 6. Gita buys 8 packets. How many biscuits does she get?

11. I spend £8·78, and pay with a £10 note. How much change do I get?

12. Put these decimals in order, smallest first: 1·3, 1·5, 1·25

13. Is an angle of 108° acute or obtuse?

14. Joanne has 35 sweets. If she shared them between 8 children, how many would they have each?

15. A fairground ride costs 75p. How many rides can Jude have for £3?

C

1   $3 \times 0 =$

2   5272, 5271, 5270, ☐

3   $58 - 12 - 24 =$

4   $237 - 116 =$

5   ☐ $\times 12 = 96$

6   $32 \div$ ☐ $= 8$

7   $46 + 23 =$

8   $\frac{1}{2} - \frac{1}{4} =$

9   $6^2 + 8 =$

10   4537, 4532, ☐, 4522

11   $-8 + 3 + 2 =$

12   $\frac{9}{3} =$

13   $(3 \times 9) + 8 =$

14   $90 \div 5 =$

15   $\frac{3}{4}$ of $16 =$

Draw 3 different shapes with an area of $9\,\text{cm}^2$

D

1   Write fifty-six thousand seven hundred and fifty-one in numerals.

2   15 thousand + 6 units + 4 tens + 2 hundreds =

3   Put these numbers in order, smallest first: 12 605, 2915, 12 506.

4   Estimate the answer to 19×6.

5   The temperature is 2°C, overnight it drops 2 degrees.
What is the new temperature?

6   What are the next two multiples of 9?
36, 45, ☐, ☐

7   What is the volume of a cube with sides measuring 2 cm?

8   What number multiplied by itself gives 81?

9   250 people are in a queue to see a film. The cinema holds 520 people. How many more people will be let in?

10   A cardigan has 9 buttons. If 72 buttons are used, how many cardigans is this?

11   Complete the ratio, 1:7, 12:☐

12   I buy two bunches of flowers at £1·50, how much change do I get from £10?

13   What is this shape?

14   Is a metre longer or shorter than a yard?

15   There are four cubes in a bag, three are red, one is blue. What chance have I got of pulling out a red one?

Exercise 2

8/10

A

1 $7 \times 6 = 42$

2 3754, 3755, ☐, 3757

2 3 $65 + 23 + 11 = 99$

3 4 $436 + 423 = 859$

4 5 $12 \times 9 = 108$

5 6 $69 - \boxed{37} = 32$

6 7 $30 \div 6 = 5$

7 8 $\frac{1}{6} + \frac{2}{3} = \frac{5}{6}$

8 9 $4^2 = 16$

10 4629, 4637, 4645, ☐

9 11 $-6 + 9 = 3$

10 12 $\frac{1}{2} = 0\cdot\boxed{5} = \boxed{50}\%$

13 $(3 \times 9) - 7 =$

11 14 $144 \div 9 = 16$

12 15 50% of 180 = 90

What are the co-ordinates for this shape?

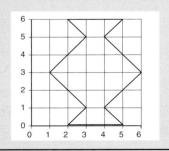

B

1 Write 18 007 in words.

2 Round 18 709 to the nearest 1000.

3 What value has the 3 in 20 309?

13 4 Is the answer to 526 + 787 nearer 1200 or (1300)?

5 Give two factors of 20.

14 6 Jenny is making a model with 20 cubes. 20% of the cubes are green. How many is this?   4

7 Name a prime number between 4 and 10.

8 $6^2 + 8 =$

7.24

15 9 Paula buys a birthday card which costs £1·25 and a present which costs £5·99. How much does she spend in total?

16 10 If there are six eggs in each box, how many eggs in 9 boxes?   54

17 11 I spend £7·62, and pay with a £10 note. How much is my change?   £2.38

12 Put these decimals in order, smallest first: 2·7, 2·69, 2·79

18 13 Is an angle of 32° (acute) or obtuse?

19 14 Stevie has 43 apples.   4 If she shared them between 9 children, how many would they have each?

20 15 Ice-creams cost 65p. How many could Tony get for £1·95?

3

C

1. $13 \times 4 = 52$

2. 4631, 4630, ☐, 4628

3. $64 - 12 - 21 = 31$

4. $468 - 234 = 234$

5. $7 \times 13 = 91$

6. $42 \div 7 = 6$

7. $52 + 37 = 89$

8. $\frac{3}{4} - \frac{1}{2} = \frac{1}{4}$

9. $3^2 + 6 = 15$

10. 2341, 2335, ☐, 2323

11. $-9 + 6 + 2 = -1$

12. $\frac{12}{4} = 3$

13. $(4 \times 6) + 7 = 31$

14. $112 \div 7 = 16$

15. $\frac{2}{3}$ of 15 = 10

Can you make 51 using + and × and all five numbers only once?

3	6
	15
4	
	14

D

1. Write forty thousand one hundred and eight in numerals.

2. 21 thousand + 2 units + 6 hundreds + 1 ten =

3. Put these numbers in order, largest first: 23 004, 2304, 24 003

4. Estimate the answer to 19×8. 152

5. The temperature is 3°C. Overnight it drops 4 degrees. What is the new temperature −1°

6. What are the next two multiples of 7? 70, 77, ☐, ☐

7. What is the volume of a cube with sides measuring 3 cm? 29 cm³

8. What number multiplied by itself gives 64?

9. There are 642 people staying at a holiday centre. At the weekend 387 people leave. How many people are left at the centre?

10. A bookshelf is filled with books whose spines are 4 cm wide. The bookshelf is 52 cm long. How many books will it hold?

11. Complete the ratio, 1:5 6:30

12. I buy three magazines at £1·45 each. How much change do I get from £10? 3.35 5.65

13. What is this shape?

14. Is a litre more or less than a pint?

15. There are six cubes in a bag. There are 2 blue cubes, 2 green cubes and 2 red cubes. What chance do I have of pulling out a green cube? $\frac{2}{6}$

Exercise 3

29/10

A

1. $4 \times 9 =$ 36

2. 6997, 6998, 6999, ☐

3. $53 + 21 + 33 =$

4. $375 + 423 =$

5. $12 \times 7 =$

6. $57 - \square = 12$

7. $45 \div 5 =$

8. $\frac{1}{5} + \frac{2}{10} = \frac{\square}{\square}$ or $\frac{\square}{\square}$

9. $6^2 =$

10. 2695, ☐, 2709, 2716

11. $-9 + 12 =$

12. $\frac{1}{3} = 0 \cdot \square = \square \%$

13. $(6 \times 8) - 10 =$

14. $90 \div 6 =$

15. 25% of 40 =

Draw 3 different shapes with a perimeter of 114 cm.

B

1. Write 22 300 in words.

2. Round 20 261 to the nearest 1000.

3. What value has the 6 in 60 409?

4. Is the answer to $289 + 763$ nearer 1000 or 1100?

5. Give two factors of 12.

6. Frances made a model using 60 cubes. 10% are white. How many is this?

7. Name a prime number between 15 and 20.

8. $2^3 + 6 =$

9. Ahmed mixes 425 g of flour with 290 g of margarine. What is the weight of the mixture?

10. There are 12 pencils in a box. How many pencils in 4 boxes?

11. I spend £6·37 and pay with a £10 note. How much is my change?

12. Put these decimals in order, smallest first: 3·37, 3·73, 3·7

13. Is an angle of 78° acute or obtuse?

14. Emma has 49 bananas. If she shared them between 8 children, how many would they have each?

15. Chocolate bars cost 45p each. How many can Desmond buy for £2·25?

C

1. $7 \times 7 =$

2. 6020, ☐, 6018, 6017

3. $97 - 32 - 24 =$

4. $537 - 126 =$

5. ☐ $\times 14 = 112$

6. $72 \div$ ☐ $= 9$

7. $34 + 45 =$

8. $\frac{1}{3} - \frac{1}{4} =$

9. $7^2 + 8 =$

10. 6258, 6251, ☐, 6237

11. $-7 + 4 + 1 =$

12. $\frac{10}{2} =$

13. $(5 \times 7) + 9 =$

14. $135 \div 9 =$

15. $\frac{4}{5}$ of 30 =

Copy and complete the Function Machine

$\times 6 - 4$

in	out
9	
12	
16	
24	
8	
15	
21	
32	
47	

D

1. Write twenty-seven thousand six hundred and ninety-four in numerals.

2. 3 units + 22 thousand + 3 hundreds + 2 tens =

3. Put these numbers in order, largest first: 16 207, 17 206, 12 706

4. Estimate the answer to 19×9.

5. The temperature is 4°C. Overnight it drops 3 degrees. What is the new temperature?

6. What are the next two multiples of 6? 72, 78, ☐, ☐

7. What is the volume of a cube with sides measuring 5 cm?

8. What number multiplied by itself gives 100?

9. Over a weekend a shop sells 256 packets of crisps. If the original stock was 528, how many packets are left?

10. Mr Jones uses 12 tea bags every day. How long will a box of 144 tea bags last?

11. Complete the ratio, 1:9, 7:☐

12. I buy 3 cakes at £1·20 each. How much change do I get from £10?

13. What is this shape?

14. Is a kilogram heavier or lighter than a pound?

15. There are three cubes in a box. Two are yellow and one is orange. What chance do I have of pulling out an orange cube?

29/10

A

1   $8 \times 3 =$ *7 × 7 49*

2   5108, 5109, ☐, 5111

3   $42 + 16 + 31 =$ *89*

4   $521 + 238 =$ *759*

5   $12 \times 8 =$ *96*

6   $35 - ☐ = 24$ *11*

7   $49 \div 7 =$ *7*

8   $\frac{1}{2} + \frac{3}{4} =$ *$\frac{5}{4}$ 1¼*

9   $9^2 =$ *81*

10   5682, 5694, ☐, 5718

11   $-4 + 8 =$ *4*

12   $\frac{1}{5} = 0 \cdot \boxed{2} = \boxed{20}\%$

13   $(2 \times 7) - 5 =$ *9*

14   $72 \div 4 =$ *18*

15   50% of 160 = *80*

Copy and complete.

+	6·14		2·01	
3·25				4·61
			6·14	
6·8		12·11		
	15·68			

B

1   Write 31 670 in words.

2   Round 23 049 to the nearest 1000.

3   What value has the 8 in 20 803?

4   Is the answer to 808 + 947 nearer 1700 or 1800? *1800*

5   Give two factors of 36. *2, 4, 6, 9, 18*

6   David made a model using 40 cubes. 20% are blue. How many is this? *8*

7   Name a prime number between 30 and 35. *31*

8   $4^2 - 3 =$

9   Chris mixes 497 ml of coke with 215 ml of lemonade. How many ml of drink does he have now?

10   There are 9 plants in each window box. How many plants in 6 boxes? *54*

11   I spend £7·13 and pay with a £10 note. How much is my change? *£2·87*

12   Put these decimals in order, smallest first: 5·9, 5·92, 5·89

13   Is an angle of 125° acute or obtuse?

14   Eric has 58 sweets. If he shared them between 7 children, how many would they have each?

15   If a paintbrush costs 85p, how many can Jimmy buy for £2·55?

C

1. $4 \times 9 =$

2. $\boxed{}$, 5011, 5010, 5009

3. $47 - 12 - 24 =$

4. $359 - 137 =$

5. $\boxed{} \times 17 = 85$

6. $54 \div \boxed{} = 6$

7. $42 + 56 =$

8. $\frac{1}{2} - \frac{1}{5} =$

9. $5^2 + 2 =$

10. 3508, $\boxed{}$, 3490, 3481

11. $-6 + 2 + 2 =$

12. $\frac{15}{5} =$

13. $(7 \times 6) + 4 =$

14. $54 \div 3 =$

15. $\frac{5}{6}$ of 48 =

Draw 3 different shapes with an area of 16 cm²

D

1. Write sixty thousand six hundred and sixty in numerals.

2. 2 hundreds + 13 thousands + 6 units =

3. Put these numbers in order, smallest first: 17 607, 607, 17 706

4. Estimate the answer to 29×5?

5. The temperature is 1°C. Overnight it rises by 3 degrees. What is the new temperature?

6. What are the next 2 multiples of 11? 121, 132, $\boxed{}$, $\boxed{}$

7. What is the volume of a cube with sides measuring 1 cm?

8. What number multiplied by itself gives 49?

9. A child must go to school for 190 days each year. How many days in a year does a child not spend in school?

10. At a quiz there are 60 people sitting at tables of 4. How many tables are there?

11. Complete the ratio, 1:9 9:$\boxed{}$

12. I buy 4 chocolate bars at 60p each. How much change do I get from £10?

13. What sort of triangle is this?

14. Is a gram heavier or lighter than an ounce?

15. There are ten socks in one drawer. 7 are brown and 3 are black. What chance have I got of pulling out a brown sock?

Exercise 5

29/10

A

14.

1   $6 \times 6 =$ 36

17   **2**   2199, 2200, 2201, 2202

14   **3** $21 + 34 + 44 =$ 99

14   **4** $372 + 416 =$ 788

20   **5** $11 \times 6 =$ 66

21   **6** $76 - 33 = 43$

22   **7** $54 \div 9 =$ 6

23   **8** $\frac{2}{3} + \frac{2}{3} = \frac{4}{3}$

24   **9** $2^2 =$ 4

25   **10**   7501, 7514, 7523, 7534

26   **11** $-8 + 15 =$ 7

27   **12** $\frac{3}{4} = 0.75 = 75\%$

28   **13** $(4 \times 9) - 3 = 33$

29   **14** $68 \div 2 =$ 34

30   **15**   25% of 160 = 40

What are the co-ordinates for this shape?

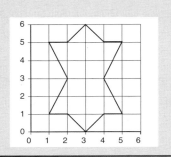

B

1   Write 39 009 in words.

2   Round 29 652 to the nearest 1000.   30,000

3   What value has the 7 in 73 028?   70,000

4   Is the answer to $987 + 719$ nearer 1600 or 1700?   1700

5   Give two factors of 18.   2,3,6,9

6   John made a model with 35 bricks. 20% are orange. How many is this?   7

7   Name a prime number between 12 and 18.   13, 17

8   $3^3 - 7 =$ 20

9   A family travel 527 km on the first day of their holiday. On the second day they travel 490 km. How far have they travelled in total?   1017

10   There are 6 videos in a pack. How many videos in 6 packs?   36

11   I spend £8·79, and pay with a £10 note. How much is my change?   £1·21

12   Put these decimals in order, smallest first: 12·12, 12·2, 12·1
      2   3   1

13   Is an angle of 26° acute or obtuse?

14   Ishmail has 70 nuts. If he shared them between 9 friends, how many would they have each?   7   r.7

15   A hot dog costs 85p. How many can Lina buy with £4·25?   5

C

1   $6 \times 1 =$

2   3287, 3286, 3285, ☐

3   $59 - 21 - 16 =$ 22

4   $638 - 406 =$ 232

5   $\boxed{9} \times 12 = 108$

6   $49 \div \boxed{7} = 7$

7   $65 + 23 =$ 88

8   $\frac{1}{4} - \frac{1}{8} =$ $\frac{1}{8}$

9   $8^2 + 9 =$ 73

10   5217, 5209, 5201, ☐

11   $-8 + 4 + 1 =$ -3

12   $\frac{12}{3} =$ 4

13   $(6 \times 3) + 5 =$ 23

14   $56 \div 4 =$ 14

15   $\frac{2}{5}$ of $35 =$ 14

Can you make 210 using + and × and all five numbers only once?

2	5
	19
3	
	17

D

1   Write forty-nine thousand eight hundred in numerals.

2   4 hundreds + 2 tens + 15 thousands + 3 units =

3   Put these numbers in order, smallest first: 16 409, 19 604, 1908

4   Estimate the answer to 29×7.   189   203

5   The temperature is 5°C. Overnight it rises by 7 degrees. What is the new temperature?   12°C

6   What are the next 2 multiples of 8? 88, 96, ☐, ☐

7   What is the volume of a cube with sides measuring 4 cm?   16×4   64 cm³

8   What number multiplied by itself gives 25?   5

9   I record a programme that lasts for 145 minutes. How many minutes are left on a 240 minute tape?   95

10   108 people attend a concert. They are seated in rows of 6 people. How many rows are there?   18

11   Complete the ratio, 1:11, 10: $\boxed{110}$

12   I buy 5 packets of biscuits at 25p each. How much change do I get from £10?

13   What is this shape?

14   Is a centimetre longer or shorter than an inch?   2:3   ⅔

15   There are 3 apples in a bag. 2 are red and 1 is green. What chance have I got of pulling out a red one?

Exercise 6

(A)

1 $5 \times 8 =$ _40_

2   9396, 9397, 9398, ☐

3 $11 + 56 + 32 =$ _99_

4 $254 + 403 =$ _657_

5 $11 \times 8 =$ _88_

6 $87 - \boxed{35} = 52$

7 $72 \div 8 =$ _9_

8 $\frac{3}{8} + \frac{1}{4} =$ _$\frac{5}{8}$_

9 $5^2 =$ _25_

10   6354, 6368, 6382, ☐

11 $-3 + 14 =$ _11_

12 $\frac{2}{5} = 0 \cdot \boxed{4} = \boxed{40}$%

13 $(8 \times 7) - 9 =$ _47_

14 $119 \div 7 =$ _17_

15   25% of 200 = _50_

☆ Draw 3 different shapes with a perimeter of 20 cm.

(B)

1   Write 42 308 in words.

2   Round 40 036 to the nearest 1000. _40 000_

3   What value has the 9 in 29 047?

4   Is the answer to $759 + 687$ nearer 1300 or 1400? _1400_

5   Give two factors of 30. _1, 2, 3, 5, 6, 15, 30_

6   Zoë made a model with 48 bricks. 25% are blue. How many is this? _12_

7   Name a prime number between 18 and 25.

8 $5^2 + 12 =$

9   Mum buys a vase for £9·95 and a bunch of flowers for £3·80. How much does she spend in total? _£13.75_

10   The school caretaker stacks chairs in piles of 7. How many chairs in 8 piles?

11   I spend £18·76, and pay with a £20 note. How much is my change? _£1.24_

12   Put these decimals in order, smallest first: 16·82, 16·28, 16·3

13   Is an angle of 179° acute or obtuse?

14   Nicky has 84 flowerpots. If she shared them between 8 friends, how many would they have each? _10 and 4 left_

15   A child's bus fare is 55p. How many children can be paid for with £2·75?

14

C

1. $8 \times 8 =$ *64*

2. 7410, ☐, 7408, 7407

3. $86 - 42 - 23 =$

4. $955 - 534 =$ *421*

5. ☐ $\times 15 = 135$

6. $48 \div$ ☐ $= 6$

7. $83 + 16 =$ *99*

8. $\frac{2}{3} - \frac{1}{4} =$ *5/12*

9. $6^2 + 4 =$ *40*

10. 8010, 8004, ☐, 7992

11. $-9 + 3 + 4 =$ *-2*

12. $\frac{20}{4} =$ *5*

13. $(8 \times 4) + 6 =$ *38*

14. $120 \div 8 =$ *15*

15. $\frac{1}{4}$ of $44 =$ *11*

Copy and complete the Function Machine
-16

in	out
59	
28	
73	
41	
22	
91	
107	
235	
348	

D

1. Write thirty-nine thousand and fifty-six in numerals.

2. 7 units + 18 thousands =

3. Put these numbers in order, largest first: 27 609, 26 907, 27 906.

4. Estimate the answer to 8×39. *320*

5. The temperature is 7°C. Overnight it drops 2 degrees. What is the new temperature?

6. What are the next 2 multiples of 12? 120, 132, ☐, ☐

7. What is the volume of a cube with sides measuring 6 cm? *36×6 = 216*

8. What number multiplied by itself gives 121? *11*

9. The book that Mrs Stewart is reading has 712 pages. She has already read 584 pages. How many pages are left to read? *128*

10. Mr Phillips has made 45 buns. He has 1 baking tray, which holds 15 buns. How many times did he have to use the tin? *3*

11. Complete the ratio, 1:8, 13:*104*

12. I buy 2 boxes of cornflakes at £2·75 each. How much change do I get from £10? *£4·50*

13. What is this shape?

14. Is a decimetre (10 cm) longer or shorter than a foot?

15. There are 4 coins in a bag. 2 are 10p, 1 is a 5p and 1 is a 2p. What chance have I got of taking out a 10p? *2:4 ½*

Exercise 7

A

1. $9 \times 7 =$

2. 7409, 7410, ☐, 7412

3. $24 + 34 + 41 =$

4. $625 + 234 =$

5. $11 \times 9 =$

6. $98 - ☐ = 35$

7. $27 \div 3 =$

8. $\frac{2}{5} + \frac{4}{5} =$

9. $8^2 =$

10. 8988, ☐, 9018, 9033

11. $-7 + 20 =$

12. $\frac{1}{10} = 0\cdot☐ = ☐\%$

13. $(5 \times 3) - 4 =$

14. $57 \div 3 =$

15. 50% of $140 =$

Copy and complete.

×		45		71
9			261	
	288			568
6				
		180		

B

1. Write 48 387 in words.

2. Round 49 207 to the nearest 1000.

3. What value has the 8 in 28 476?

4. Is the answer to $826 + 987$ nearer 1700 or 1800?

5. Give two factors of 16.

6. Fiona builds a model with 72 bricks. 25% are red. How many is this?

7. Name a prime number between 21 and 30.

8. $6^2 - 8 =$

9. The greengrocer sells 129 kg of black grapes and 293 kg of white grapes. How many kg of grapes does he sell altogether?

10. There are 12 eggs in a dozen. How many eggs in five dozen?

11. I spend £17·62, and pay with a £20 note. How much is my change?

12. Put these decimals in order, smallest first: 20·02, 20·20, 20·12

13. Is an angle of 89° acute or obtuse?

14. Amanda has 78 marbles. If she shared them between 8 friends, how many would they have each?

15. Pens cost 72p each. How many can Andrew buy if he has £3·60?

(C)

1 $4 \times 8 =$

2 ☐ , 8339, 8338, 8337

3 $77 - 32 - 24 =$

4 $748 - 524 =$

5 ☐ $\times 16 = 128$

6 $64 \div$ ☐ $= 8$

7 $74 + 13 =$

8 $\frac{2}{3} - \frac{1}{2} =$

9 $9^2 + 5 =$

10 7421, 7412, 7403, ☐

11 $-7 + 3 + 2 =$

12 $\frac{12}{2} =$

13 $(2 \times 7) + 5 =$

14 $96 \div 6 =$

15 $\frac{3}{5}$ of $45 =$

Draw 3 different shapes with an area of $24 \, cm^2$.

(D)

1 Write seventy-nine thousand four hundred and six in numerals.

2 4 tens + 3 units + 14 thousands =

3 Put these numbers in order, smallest first: 14 732, 12 742, 12 744

4 Estimate the answer to 48×6.

5 The temperature is $-7°C$. Overnight the temperature rises by 5 degrees. What is the new temperature?

6 What are the next two multiples of 9? 90, 99, ☐ , ☐

7 What is the volume of a cube with sides measuring 10 cm?

8 What number multiplied by itself gives 36?

9 There are 433 children in the school. 289 school dinners have been ordered. How many children are not having dinners?

10 At a netball tournament, 128 children are taking part. The teams each have 8 players, including a reserve. How many teams are taking part?

11 Complete the ratio, 1:13, 4:☐

12 I buy 4 bottles of lemonade at £1·10 each. How much change do I get from £10?

13 What is this shape?

14 Is a foot longer or shorter than a metre?

15 Sarah is in a race with 3 other people. What chance does she have of winning?

Exercise 8

A

1. $7 \times 5 =$

2. ☐, 8450, 8451, 8452

3. $26 + 32 + 53 =$

4. $754 + 205 =$

5. $12 \times 10 =$

6. $67 - ☐ = 24$

7. $36 \div 6 =$

8. $\frac{1}{3} + \frac{4}{6} =$

9. $7^2 =$

10. 9462, 9474, 9786, ☐

11. $-7 + 16 =$

12. $\frac{3}{5} = 0.☐ = ☐\%$

13. $(6 \times 2) - 8 =$

14. $126 \div 9 =$

15. 25% of $80 =$

What are the co-ordinates for this shape?

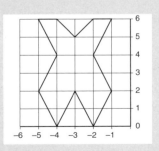

B

1. Write 89 400 in words.

2. Round 99 608 to the nearest 1000.

3. What value has the 6 in 68 982?

4. Is the answer to $657 + 875$ nearer 1500 or 1600?

5. Give two factors of 48.

6. Frank makes a model with 56 cubes. 25% are orange. How many is this?

7. Name a prime number between 25 and 34.

8. $8^2 + 16 =$

9. There are 376 pupils in the infant school and 451 in the junior school. How many pupils altogether?

10. In assembly, 9 children sit in each row. How many children are there in 8 rows?

11. I spend £15·08, and pay with a £20 note. How much is my change?

12. Put these decimals in order, smallest first: 27·27, 27·2, 27·72

13. Is an angle of 78° acute or obtuse?

14. Victoria has 58 stamps. If she shared them between 7 friends, how many would they have each?

15. A bag of popcorn costs 67p. How many can I buy with £3·35?

C

1. $9 \times 5 =$

2. 2705, 2704, 2703, ☐

3. $98 - 36 - 21 =$

4. $866 - 425 =$

5. ☐ $\times 16 = 144$

6. $63 \div$ ☐ $= 7$

7. $72 + 24 =$

8. $\frac{4}{5} - \frac{1}{10} =$

9. $4^2 + 10 =$

10. ☐, 4351, 4345, 4339

11. $-6 + 0 + 4 =$

12. $\frac{30}{5} =$

13. $(8 \times 8) + 2 =$

14. $76 \div 4 =$

15. $\frac{1}{5}$ of 60 =

Can you make 284 using – and × and these five numbers only once?

7	6	
		24
4		17

D

1. Write eighty-three thousand two hundred and nine in numerals.

2. 3 units + 18 thousands =

3. Put these numbers in order, largest first: 7676, 767, 7767

4. Estimate the answer to 52×7.

5. The temperature is −4°C. Overnight it rises by 4 degrees. What is the new temperature?

6. What are the next two multiples of 7? 98, 105, ☐, ☐

7. What is the volume of a cube with sides measuring 7 cm?

8. What number multiplied by itself gives 144?

9. In a survey of 776 people, 487 said their favourite TV programme was 'Coronation Street'. How many people had a different favourite?

10. Lucy's dad ordered cans of lemonade from the supermarket. He ordered 75 cans in packs of 15. How many packs were there?

11. Complete the ratio, 12:4, 3:☐

12. I buy 2 tickets for the cinema at £3·25 each. How much change do I get from £10?

13. What is this shape?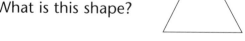

14. Is a mile longer or shorter than 1 km?

15. There are 8 sweets in a packet. There are the same number of strawberry, lemon, lime and orange. What chance have I got of getting a lemon one?

Exercise 9

A

1. $8 \times 6 =$

2. 4379, ☐, 4381, 4382

3. $31 + 42 + 56 =$

4. $428 + 342 =$

5. $11 \times 10 =$

6. $46 - ☐ = 11$

7. $32 \div 4 =$

8. $\frac{1}{4} + \frac{1}{4} =$

9. $1^2 =$

10. 3002, ☐, 3038, 3056

11. $-5 + 30 =$

12. $\frac{2}{3} = 0 \cdot ☐ = ☐\%$

13. $(4 \times 3) - 6 =$

14. $104 \div 8 =$

15. 50% of 90 =

Draw 3 different shapes with a perimeter of 16 cm.

B

1. Write 96 908 in words.

2. Round 108 207 to the nearest 1000.

3. What value has the 7 in 117 681?

4. Is the answer to $816 + 887$ nearer 1600 or 1700?

5. Give 2 factors of 72.

6. Sheila builds a model with 84 bricks. 25% are green. How many is this?

7. Name a prime number between 32 and 45.

8. $11^2 + 6 =$

9. The fabric shop sold 212 m of striped fabric and 696 m of plain fabric in one week. How much was sold altogether?

10. The teacher puts 7 paintings on each display board. She uses 7 display boards altogether. How many paintings does she display?

11. I spend £13·13, and pay with a £20 note. How much is my change?

12. Put these decimals in order, smallest first: 36·17, 36·7, 36·71

13. Is an angle of 31° acute or obtuse?

14. Natalie has 150 pencils. If she shared them between 12 friends, how many would they have each?

15. Yo-yos are 57p each. How many can I buy for £4·56?

C

1. $7 \times 8 =$

2. 9741, 9740, ☐, 9738

3. $69 - 13 - 35 =$

4. $457 - 236 =$

5. ☐ $\times 19 = 152$

6. $24 \div$ ☐ $= 6$

7. $21 + 75 =$

8. $\frac{5}{6} - \frac{1}{3} =$

9. $7^2 + 7 =$

10. ☐, 2601, 2593, 2585

11. $-8 + 3 + 4 =$

12. $\frac{24}{6} =$

13. $(4 \times 4) + 3 =$

14. $108 \div 6 =$

15. $\frac{2}{7}$ of $42 =$

Copy and complete the Function Machine

÷8

in	out
72	
96	
120	
112	
144	
168	
200	
240	
328	

D

1. Write forty thousand and eight in numerals.

2. 17 thousands + 2 units + 2 tens =

3. Put these numbers in order, smallest first: 12 912, 91 212, 21 912

4. Estimate the answer to 9×61.

5. The temperature is –8°C. Overnight it rises by 3 degrees. What is the new temperature?

6. What are the next two multiples of 8? 104, 112, ☐, ☐

7. What is the volume of a cube with sides measuring 9 cm?

8. What number multiplied by itself gives 16?

9. 846 spectators are watching a football match. If 688 support team A, how many spectators support team B?

10. A farmer planted 120 new trees in rows of 15. How many rows are there?

11. Complete the ratio, 1:15 5:☐

12. I buy 3 plants at £1·75 each. How much change do I get from 10?

13. What is this shape?

14. Is a kilogram heavier or lighter than a stone?

15. What chance have I got of getting an even number if I throw a 1–6 dice?

Exercise 10

(A)

1. $3 \times 9 =$ *27*

2. 5008, 5009, ☐, 5011

3. $86 + 21 + 43 =$ *150*

4. $555 + 244 =$ *799*

5. $12 \times 5 =$ *60*

6. $58 - \boxed{34} = 24$

7. $21 \div 7 =$

8. $\frac{1}{2} + \frac{1}{6} =$ *4/6 2/3*

9. $10^2 =$ *100*

10. 8257, 8274, 8291, ☐

11. $-8 + 16 =$ *8*

12. $\frac{4}{5} = 0 \cdot \boxed{8} = \boxed{80}\%$

13. $(6 \times 7) - 9 =$ *33*

14. $102 \div 6 =$ *17*

15. 50% of $270 =$ *135*

⭐ **Copy and complete.**

×		4·78	9·01	
7	22·47			
			81·09	
		23·9		
8				45·84

(B)

1. Write 99 999 in words.

2. Round 119 862 to the nearest 1000.

3. What value has the 1 in 123 456?

4. Is the answer to $587 + 768$ nearer 1300 or 1400?

5. Give two factors of 64. *2 32, 4 16, 8, 8.*

6. Stefan builds a model with 120 cubes. 10% are black. How many is this?

7. Name a prime number between 42 and 56. *43 47 53*

8. $12^2 + 16 =$

9. In a survey, 1326 children said the Big Wheel was their favourite funfair ride. 272 preferred the Dodgems. How many children were surveyed? *1598*

10. Wanda puts 6 apples in each bag. How many apples will go into 8 bags?

11. I spend £11·62, and pay with a £20 note. How much is my change? *8.38*

12. Put these decimals in order, smallest first: 106·47, 106·74, 106·40

13. Is an angle of 143° acute or obtuse?

14. Jimmy has 112 stickers. If she shared them between 11 children, how many would they have each? *10 r2*

15. Ice-lollies are 87p each. How many can be bought for £4·35? *5*

C

1   $9 \times 9 =$

2   5639, 5638, ☐, 5636

3   $79 - 42 - 17 =$

4   $528 - 416 =$

5   ☐ $\times 18 = 126$

6   $40 \div$ ☐ $= 8$

7   $37 + 43 =$

8   $\frac{3}{5} - \frac{1}{10} =$ $\frac{5}{10}$ $\frac{1}{2}$

9   $4^2 + 3 =$ 19 *(6)*

10 6003, ☐, 5991, 5985

11 $-9 + 5 + 4 =$

12 $\frac{56}{8} =$

13 $(9 \times 5) + 3 =$ 48 *(20)*

14 $98 \div 7 =$ 14 *(7.)*

15 $\frac{3}{8}$ of $56 =$ 21 *(8.)*

Draw 3 different shapes with an area of 32 cm².

D   *98807*   *(18)*

1   Write ninety-eight thousand eight hundred and seven in numerals.

2   8 tens + 3 units + 19 thousands + 4 hundreds =

3   Put these numbers in order, largest first: 27 297, 29 729, 7920

4   Estimate the answer to 4×91 to the nearest ten.   *400 360*   *(9.)*

5   The temperature is –7°C. Overnight it drops another 3 degrees. What is the new temperature? -10 *(10.)*

6   What are the next 2 multiples of 11? 176, 187, 198, 209   *(11.)*

7   What is the volume of a cube with sides measuring 8 cm? $64 \times 8 = 512$ *(12)*

8   What number multiplied by itself gives 49?   *(19)*

9   There are 972 cars in a 2-storey car park. If there are 587 cars on the first floor, how many are parked on the second floor?   *(13. 385)*

10 72 children go on a school trip. 4 children sleep in each room. How many rooms are needed?   *(18) (14.)*

11 Complete the ratio, 1:18   3:54   *(15)*

12 I buy 3 books at £2·45 each. How much change do I get from £10?   *(16 £2·65)*

13 What is this shape?

14 Is a gallon more or less than a litre?   *(17)*

15 In my purse there are three 20p pieces, two 2p pieces and one 1p piece. What is the chance of my taking out a bronze coin?   *(17) $\frac{3}{6}$*

Exercise 11

A

1. $5 \times \boxed{} = 35$

2. 23 475, 23 476, 23 477, $\boxed{}$

3. $56 + 22 + 15 =$

4. $423 + 128 =$

5. $14 \times 5 =$

6. $72 - \boxed{} = 37$

7. $19 \div 3 = 5 \text{ r } \boxed{}$

8. $1\frac{2}{3} + \frac{2}{3} =$

9. $2^3 =$

10. 47 371, 47 380, 47 389, $\boxed{}$

11. $0.75 = \frac{3}{4} = \boxed{}\%$

12. $-12 + 6 =$

13. $(7 \times 8) - 16 =$

14. $52 \div 3 = 17 \text{ r } \boxed{}$

15. $1.3 + 2.9 =$

What are the co-ordinates for this shape?

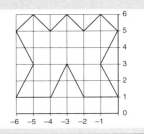

B

1. Write 38·6 in words.

2. What value has the 6 in 26·73?

3. What is the product of 8 and 9?

4. How many times does 16 go into 50?

5. $23 \div 10 =$

6. $4200 \div 60 = 70$

7. Is 16 a factor of 48?

8. Write 1·00 am using the 24 hour clock.

9. 385 people attended a school concert on Monday and 397 people on Tuesday. How many attended altogether?

10. During the school holidays, Joe watches TV for 4 hours each day. How many hours is this a fortnight?

11. (2^2) to power of three =

12. Does this net make a cube?

13. What is the perimeter of a rectangle measuring 6 cm x 3 cm?

14. Increase £10 by 50%.

15. Two of the angles in a triangle equal 90°. What is the third angle?

C

1. $\square \times 3 = 18$

2. 43 110, $\boxed{}$, 43 108, 43 107

3. $76 - 47 =$

4. $456 - 138 =$

5. $23 \times 2 =$

6. $26 \div 4 = \square \ r\ 2$

7. $38 + 47 =$

8. $1\frac{2}{5} - \frac{3}{10} =$

9. $4^2 - 9 =$

10. 54 274, 54 264, 54 254, $\boxed{}$

11. $-12 + 4 - 6 =$

12. $\frac{3}{12} = \frac{\square}{4}$

13. $(4 \times 9) + 18 =$

14. $37 \div 2 = \square \ r\ 1$

15. 40% of 90 =

Can you make 92 using – and × and all five numbers only once.

3	4
26	7
	32

D

1. Write thirty-eight point seven in numerals.

2. 15 thousands + 2 units + 4 hundreds =

3. Round 2·75 to the nearest whole number.

4. $0·2 \times 10 =$

5. Continue the pattern: 21, 15, 11, $\square$, $\square$

6. $2100 \times 40 =$

7. Is 98 a multiple of 7?

8. What is the volume of a cuboid with sides measuring 1 cm, 2 cm and 3 cm?

9. By midday the Wilson family had travelled 362 km. The total distance, to be travelled was 1290 km.
How many km had they still to go?

10. Jane has 60 pencils. They are in packs of 15. How many packs has she got?

11. Complete the ratio, 12:36   1:$\square$

12. I buy 3 boxes of chocolate which cost £3·50 each. How much change will I get from £20?

13. What is the area of a shape measuring 8 cm by 4 cm?

14. The scores in a test were: 63, 72, 63, 65, 70, 63. What is the mode?

15. 5 phone calls are made. 3 calls are made by men and 2 by women.
What is the probability of a caller being a man?

Exercise 12

A

1. $6 \times \boxed{} = 42$

2. 42 167, 42 168, 42 169, $\boxed{}$

3. $35 + 24 + 36 =$

4. $267 + 315 =$

5. $15 \times 7 =$

6. $61 - \boxed{} = 36$

7. $27 \div 4 = 6 \text{ r } \boxed{}$

8. $2\frac{1}{4} + \frac{1}{4} =$

9. $3^3 =$

10. 61 543, $\boxed{}$, 61 567, 61 579

11. $0{\cdot}5 = \frac{1}{2} = \boxed{}\%$

12. $-10 + 5 =$

13. $(6 \times 3) - 12 =$

14. $62 \div 4 = 15 \text{ r } \boxed{}$

15. $2{\cdot}5 + 4{\cdot}6 =$

Draw 3 different shapes with a perimeter of 18 cm.

B

1. Write 1634 in words.

2. What value has the 8 in 8374?

3. What is the product of 12 and 10?

4. Estimate how many times does 8 go into 90?

5. $67 \div 10 =$

6. $6300 \div 90 =$

7. Is 18 a factor of 48?

8. Write 3·15 pm using the 24 hour clock.

9. During the first hour of a telephone competition, 937 people rang. 849 people telephoned in the second hour. How many people rang altogether?

10. Every week Susan saves £3. How much will she have saved after 26 weeks?

11. $(3^2)^2 =$

12. Does this net make a cube?

13. What is the perimeter of a rectangle measuring 4 cm x 5 cm?

14. Increase £10 by 25%.

15. Two of the angles in a triangle equal 120°. What is the third angle?

C

1. $\square \times 4 = 28$

2. 37 002, 37 001, 37 000, $\square$

3. $26 - 17 =$

4. $348 - 219 =$

5. $48 \times 7 =$

6. $13 \div 3 = \square$ r 1

7. $58 + 38 =$

8. $5\frac{2}{3} - \frac{1}{3} =$

9. $9^2 - 7 =$

10. 87 301, 87 201, 87 101, $\square$

11. $-15 + 8 - 6 =$

12. $\frac{15}{36} = \frac{\square}{12}$

13. $(7 \times 8) + 13 =$

14. $59 \div 4 = \square$ r $\square$

15. 70% of 60 =

Copy and complete the Function Machine

$\times 7 + 2$

in	out
8	
12	
	93
18	
	156
26	
35	
	289
52	

D

1. Write forty-nine point one in numerals.

2. 2 units + 17 thousands + 8 tens =

3. Round 1·8 to the nearest whole number.

4. $0·7 \times 10 =$

5. Continue the pattern: 17, 10, 3, $\square$, $\square$

6. $2600 \times 50 =$

7. Is 85 a multiple of 8?

8. What is the volume of a cuboid with sides measuring 2 cm, 2 cm and 3 cm?

9. The newsagent received 2325 newspapers each day. 405 were delivered by the newspaper delivery staff.
How many were left to sell in the shop?

10. The children are asked to line up in groups of 12. There are 84 children.
How many lines are there?

11. Complete the ratio, 7:42   1:$\square$

12. I buy 4 cartons of juice at £1·25 each. How much change do I get from £20?

13. What is the area of a shape measuring 9 cm by 12cm?

14. Books have the following number of pages: 107, 109, 107, 110.
What is the mode?

15. There are 10 toys in a lucky dip. 5 are cars. 5 are dolls. What is the probability of picking a toy car?

Exercise 13

A

1. $2 \times \boxed{} = 14$

2. $84\,298, 84\,299, \boxed{}, 84\,301$

3. $27 + 43 + 19 =$

4. $416 + 257 =$

5. $16 \times 5 =$

6. $53 - \boxed{} = 29$

7. $47 \div 9 = 5 \text{ r } \boxed{}$

8. $3\frac{1}{2} + \frac{1}{6} =$

9. $4^3 =$

10. $42\,593, \boxed{}, 42\,621, 42\,635$

11. $0.25 = \frac{1}{4} = \boxed{}\%$

12. $-16 + 7 =$

13. $(5 \times 7) - 19 =$

14. $124 \div 7 = 17 \text{ r } \boxed{}$

15. $6.7 + 1.5 =$

Copy and complete.

÷	6			9
24		6		2.66
	10.5			
48			6.8	
				14

B

1. Write 17·95 in words.

2. What value has the 3 in 27·93?

3. What is the product of 13 and 3?

4. How many times does 16 go into 50?

5. $321 \div 10 =$

6. $8100 \div 90 =$

7. Is 12 a factor of 50?

8. Write 1800 using the 12 hour clock.

9. In her stamp collection, Kelly has 684 stamps in one album and 578 stamps in another. How many stamps does she have altogether?

10. If each of the 30 children in orange class is 11 years old, how many years have they been alive altogether?

11. (1^3) to power of 3 =

12. Does this net make a cube?

13. What is the perimeter of a rectangle measuring $12\,\text{m} \times 1\,\text{m}$?

14. Increase 20 by 20%.

15. Two of the angles in a triangle equal 110°. What is the third angle?

C

1. $\square \times 5 = 40$

2. 79 511, 79 510, $\boxed{}$, 79 508

3. $63 - 26 =$

4. $736 - 638 =$

5. $76 \times 9 =$

6. $52 \div 8 = \square$ r 4

7. $45 + 49 =$

8. $3\frac{4}{5} - \frac{1}{5} =$

9. $7^2 - 9 =$

10. $\boxed{}$, 94 278, 93 278, 92 278

11. $-20 + 6 - 7 =$

12. $\frac{16}{24} = \frac{\square}{6}$

13. $(6 \times 3) + 15 =$

14. $50 \div 3 = \square$ r 2

15. 80% of 120 =

Draw 3 different shapes with an area of 28 cm².

D

1. Write one hundred and seven point nine in numerals.

2. 21 thousands + 6 units =

3. Round 2·4 to the nearest whole number.

4. $0·9 \times 10 =$

5. Continue the pattern: 24, 13, 2, $\boxed{}$, $\boxed{}$

6. $2700 \times 30 =$

7. Is 89 a multiple of 9?

8. What is the volume of a cuboid with sides measuring 3 cm, 2 cm and 3 cm?

9. Donald had saved £52·73. He bought a game costing £5·95.
How much did he have left?

10. There are 65 cars in a car park. They are parked in groups of 5.
How many groups are there?

11. Complete the ratio, 9:54 1:$\square$

12. I buy 4 files which cost £1·95 each.
How much change do I get from £20?

13. What is the area of a shape measuring 7 m by 14 m?

14. The results at football matches were:
3–2, 1–0, 1–1, 3–2, 2–1, 3–4.
What is the mode?

15. There are 10 shoes under a bed. 2 shoes are brown and 8 shoes are black. What is the probability of finding a brown shoe?

Exercise 14

A

1. $8 \times \boxed{} = 56$

2. $89\,998, 89\,999, \boxed{}, 90\,001$

3. $39 + 14 + 33 =$

4. $607 + 248 =$

5. $17 \times 6 =$

6. $64 - \boxed{} = 37$

7. $41 \div 5 = 8 \text{ r } \boxed{}$

8. $\frac{1}{6} + 1\frac{2}{3} =$

9. $5^3 =$

10. $36\,875, 36\,888, \boxed{}, 36\,914$

11. $0 \cdot 125 = \boxed{} = \boxed{} \%$

12. $-14 + 9 =$

13. $(8 \times 4) - 27 =$

14. $97 \div 6 = 16 \text{ r } \boxed{}$

15. $3 \cdot 2 + 2 \cdot 8 =$

What are the co-ordinates for this shape?

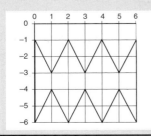

B

1. Write 272.9 in words.

2. What value has the 8 in 63·8?

3. What is the product of 15 and 4?

4. How many times does 7 go into 100?

5. $821 \div 10 =$

6. $5400 \div 60 =$

7. Is 8 a factor of 100?

8. Write 11·45 am using the 24 hour clock.

9. Jack and Patrick went out for a meal. Jack's meal cost £3·85 and Patrick's cost £3·95. How much was the bill altogether?

10. There are 8 classes in the school and each class has 700 building blocks.
How many blocks are there in school altogether?

11. $(3^2)^2 =$

12. Does this net make a cube?

13. What is the perimeter of a rectangle measuring 8 cm × 7 cm?

14. Increase £20 by 50%.

15. Two of the angles in a triangle equal 135°. What is the third angle?

C

1 $\boxed{} \times 7 = 63$

2 52 341, 52 340, $\boxed{}$, 52 338

3 $83 - 45 =$

4 $961 - 524 =$

5 $37 \times 6 =$

6 $87 \div 9 = \boxed{}$ r 6

7 $63 + 28 =$

8 $4\frac{1}{3} - \frac{2}{3} =$

9 $2^2 - 1 =$

10 73 290, 73 190, 73 090, $\boxed{}$

11 $-14 + 7 - 9 =$

12 $\frac{9}{18} = \frac{\boxed{}}{2}$

13 $(7 \times 5) + 14 =$

14 $78 \div 5 = \boxed{}$ r 3

15 40% of 50 =

Can you make 118 using + and × and all five numbers only once

9	4
	37
2	
	48

D

1 Write two hundred and sixteen point three in numerals.

2 2 tenths + 3 hundreds + 4 tens + 1 unit =

3 Round 8·14 to the nearest whole number.

4 $2·4 \times 10 =$

5 Continue the pattern: 25, 12, –1, $\boxed{}$, $\boxed{}$

6 $2500 \times 50 =$

7 Is 103 a multiple of 3?

8 What is the volume of a cuboid with sides measuring 3 cm, 2 cm and 2 cm?

9 Marie had collected 1009 different stickers. 475 were football stickers. How many stickers were not football ones?

10 The plates are stacked in piles of 15. There are 90 plates. How many piles?

11 Complete the ratio, 9:81   1:$\boxed{}$

12 I buy 4 bunches of flowers at £2·25 each. How much change will I get from £20?

13 What is the area of a shape measuring 13 cm by 13 cm?

14 Over a week, the temperatures were 21°C, 20°C, 22°C, 20°C, 21°C, 21°C. What is the mode?

15 There are 6 sweets in a bag. 4 are strawberry flavour and 2 are lemon flavour. What is the probability of choosing a lemon flavoured sweet?

A

1 $4 \times \boxed{} = 36$

2 51 008, 51 009, $\boxed{}$, 51 011

3 $67 + 13 + 16 =$

4 $355 + 316 =$

5 $18 \times 7 =$

6 $33 - \boxed{} = 14$

7 $23 \div 7 = 3 \text{ r } \boxed{}$

8 $2\frac{1}{5} + \frac{2}{10} =$

9 $5^4 =$

10 52 351, 52 362, 52 373, $\boxed{}$

11 $0\cdot2 = \boxed{} = \boxed{}\%$

12 $-17 + 10 =$

13 $(7 \times 6) - 25 =$

14 $95 \div 7 = 13 \text{ r } \boxed{}$

15 $5\cdot6 + 1\cdot7 =$

B

1 Write 1529·7 in words.

2 What value has the 2 in 312·7?

3 What is the product of 15 and 7?

4 How many times does 9 go into 120?

5 $467 \div 10 =$

6 $4800 \div 30 =$

7 Is 12 a factor of 120?

8 Write 17·10 using the 12 hour clock.

9 Josephine has a collection of soft toys. She has 285 teddy-bears and 138 other animals. How many toys altogether?

10 A shop sells candles in bundles of 9. On Saturday 20 bundles were sold. How many candles is this?

11 $(2^3)^2 =$

12 Does this net make a cube?

13 What is the perimeter of a rectangle measuring 13 m $\times$ 3 m?

14 Increase £10 by 10%.

15 Two of the angles in a triangle equal 115°. What is the third angle?

Draw 3 different shapes with a perimeter of 12 cm.

C

1. $\square \times 8 = 32$

2. 98 653, $\boxed{}$, 98 651, 98 650

3. $42 - 27 =$

4. $834 - 409 =$

5. $65 \times 8 =$

6. $31 \div 7 = \square \text{ r } 3$

7. $46 + 35 =$

8. $3\frac{1}{2} - \frac{1}{5} =$

9. $4^2 - 5 =$

10. $\boxed{}$, 32 900, 32 800, 32 700

11. $-19 + 3 - 5 =$

12. $\frac{16}{20} = \frac{\square}{5}$

13. $(5 \times 9) + 17 =$

14. $93 \div 7 = \square \text{ r } 2$

15. 60% of 80 =

Copy and complete the Function Machine
$\times 4 - 3$

in	out
12	
	97
32	
16	
	69
27	
	185
53	
	241

D

1. Write seven hundred and eight point two three in numerals.

2. 3 units + 5 tenths + 4 tens + 7 hundreds =

3. Round 8·6 to the nearest whole number.

4. $8·5 \times 10 =$

5. Continue the pattern: 20, 11, 2, $\boxed{}$, $\boxed{}$

6. $1300 \times 50 =$

7. Is 128 a multiple of 8?

8. What is the volume of a cuboid with sides measuring 5 cm, 2 cm and 5 cm?

9. Kirsten had £95·61 in her savings account. She withdrew £9·50. How much was left?

10. Mary has 144 stickers. 12 fit on a page. How many pages can she fill?

11. Complete the ratio, 12:120   1:$\square$

12. I buy 3 books which cost £3·50 each. How much change do I get from £20?

13. What is the area of a shape measuring 8 m by 16 m?

14. These are amounts in money boxes: 89p, £1·12, £1·10, £1·12, £1·00. What is the mode?

15. There are 20 football stickers in a box. 8 are Manchester United stickers. What is the probability of picking a Manchester United sticker?

Exercise 16

A

1. $10 \times \boxed{} = 50$

2. 49 657, 49 658, 49 659, $\boxed{}$

3. $46 + 24 + 22 =$

4. $634 + 238 =$

5. $13 \times 9 =$

6. $82 - \boxed{} = 38$

7. $59 \div 9 = 6 \text{ r } \boxed{}$

8. $\frac{3}{8} + 2\frac{1}{4} =$

9. $2^4 =$

10. 93 987, $\boxed{}$, 94 015, 94 029

11. $0.1 = \boxed{} = \boxed{}\%$

12. $-15 + 3 =$

13. $(6 \times 6) - 27 =$

14. $115 \div 8 = 14 \text{ r } \boxed{}$

15. $2.7 + 3.4 =$

Copy and complete.

–	5·31			9·55
37		28·97		
	22·69			
41			28·36	
				6·45

B

1. Write 2043·61 in words.

2. What value has the 5 in 232·51?

3. What is the product of 15 and 5?

4. How many times does 12 go into 100?

5. $31.2 \div 10 =$

6. $3600 \div 120 =$

7. Is 17 a factor of 70?

8. Write 12·25 am using the 24 hour clock.

9. 712 people live in one block of flats and 859 live in the neighbouring block. How many people altogether?

10. 20 people each paid £3·50 for a cinema ticket. How much did they pay altogether?

11. $(1^4)^4 =$

12. Does this net make a cube?

13. What is the perimeter of a rectangle measuring 17 cm × 4 cm?

14. Increase £15 by 10%.

15. Two of the angles in a triangle equal 140°. What is the third angle?

(C)

1 $\square \times 9 = 54$

2 20 001, 20 000, $\square$, 19 998

3 $31 - 16 =$

4 $565 - 328 =$

5 $89 \times 5 =$

6 $37 \div 4 = \square$ r 1

7 $74 + 18 =$

8 $1\frac{3}{4} - \frac{1}{4} =$

9 $3^2 - 4 =$

10 42 037, 41 937, $\square$, 41 737

11 $-17 + 9 - 2 =$

12 $\frac{2}{4} = \frac{\square}{2}$

13 $(8 \times 4) + 16 =$

14 $81 \div 6 = \square$ r 3

15 90% of 70 =

Draw 3 different shapes with an area of 42 cm².

(D)

1 Write three hundred and eight point five two in numerals.

2 3 tenths + 4 units + 7 tens + 8 hundreds =

3 Round 13·49 to the nearest whole number.

4 $27 \times 10 =$

5 Continue the pattern: 36, 23, 10, $\square$, $\square$

6 $3500 \times 30 =$

7 Is 105 a multiple of 15?

8 What is the volume of a cuboid with sides measuring 4 cm, 5 cm and 6 cm?

9 A greengrocer had 1762 kg of potatoes. During the day he sold 650 kg of potatoes. How many kg had he left at the end of the day?

10 There are 48 cakes, 4 cakes on each plate. How many plates are there?

11 Complete the ratio, 4:48 1:$\square$

12 I buy 8 bars of chocolate at 75 p each. How much change do I get from £20?

13 What is the area of a shape measuring 8 cm by 20 cm?

14 Sandwiches in a shop cost 99p, £1·09, £1·29, 99p, £1·06. What is the mode?

15 There are 15 pencils in a box. 5 pencils are yellow. 10 pencils are red. What is the probability of picking a yellow pencil?

Exercise 17

A

1. $6 \times \boxed{} = 54$

2. $\boxed{}$, 78 211, 78 212, 78 213

3. $55 + 27 + 19 =$

4. $523 + 168 =$

5. $17 \times 9 =$

6. $80 - \boxed{} = 43$

7. $30 \div 7 = 4 \text{ r } \boxed{}$

8. $4\frac{1}{3} + \frac{4}{6} =$

9. $3^4 =$

10. $\boxed{}$, 71 004, 71 020, 71 036

11. $0.01 = \boxed{} = \boxed{}\%$

12. $-18 + 4 =$

13. $(8 \times 9) - 45 =$

14. $59 \div 3 = 19 \text{ r } \boxed{}$

15. $1.4 + 7.7 =$

What are the co-ordinates for this shape?

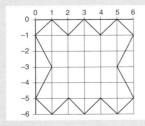

B

1. Write 8093·67 in words.

2. What value has the 8 in 239·18?

3. What is the product of 14 and 100?

4. How many times does 14 go into 100?

5. $488 \div 10 =$

6. $1500 \div 250 =$

7. Is 9 a factor of 127?

8. Write 18·45 using the 12 hour clock.

9. Chris collects postcards. She has 319 from the British Isles and 578 from Europe. How many postcards in her collection?

10. It cost 25p for a school raffle ticket. If 20 children buy a ticket, how much money is collected?

11. $(2^2)^2 + 3 =$

12. Does this net make a cube?

13. What is the perimeter of a rectangle measuring $25\,\text{m} \times 4\,\text{m}$?

14. Increase £20 by 10%.

15. Two of the angles in a triangle equal 96°. What is the third angle?

C

1. $\square \times 4 = 36$

2. $\square$, 73 199, 73 198, 73 197

3. $77 - 59 =$

4. $325 - 107 =$

5. $57 \times 2 =$

6. $53 \div 6 = \square$ r 5

7. $27 + 64 =$

8. $2\frac{3}{5} - \frac{4}{5} =$

9. $7^2 - 6 =$

10. $\square$, 56 342, 55 342, 54 342

11. $-13 + 5 - 4 =$

12. $\frac{12}{16} = \frac{\square}{4}$

13. $(2 \times 7) + 14 =$

14. $43 \div 3 = \square$ r 1

15. 20% of 40 =

Can you make 89 using +, − and × and all five numbers only once

4	7
	14
59	
	72

D

1. Write five hundred point seven two in numerals.

2. 16 units + 7 tens + 11 thousands + 2 tenths =

3. Round 17·81 to the nearest whole number.

4. $63·6 \times 10 =$

5. Continue the pattern: 17, 9, 1, $\square$, $\square$

6. $4500 \times 40 =$

7. Is 108 a multiple of 4?

8. What is the volume of a cuboid with sides measuring 6 cm, 2 cm and 4 cm?

9. The warehouse had 5050 dresses. 960 were delivered to a shop. How many were left?

10. 70 children are staying to dinner. 5 children sit round each table. How many tables are needed?

11. Complete the ratio, 12:72   1:$\square$

12. I buy 5 cakes at £1·20 each. How much change do I get from £20?

13. What is the area of a plane shape measuring 15 m by 4 m?

14. Ribbons come in these lengths: 50 cm, 125 cm, 100 cm, 125 cm, 100 cm, 125 cm. What is the mode?

15. There are 12 coins in a bag. 4 of the coins are silver. What is the probability of picking a silver coin?

Exercise 18

1. $7 \times \boxed{} = 21$

2. 69 997, 69 998, 69 999, $\boxed{}$

3. $63 + 29 + 21 =$

4. $234 + 426 =$

5. $16 \times 6 =$

6. $75 - \boxed{} = 59$

7. $60 \div 8 = 7 \text{ r } \boxed{}$

8. $\frac{1}{2} + 3\frac{3}{4} =$

9. $4^4 =$

10. 23 509, 23 526, 23 543, $\boxed{}$

11. $0.6 = \boxed{} = \boxed{}\%$

12. $-11 + 8 =$

13. $(5 \times 10) - 36 =$

14. $71 \div 5 = 14 \text{ r } \boxed{}$

15. $5.5 + 1.6 =$

(B)

1. Write 1069·23 in words.

2. What value has the 8 in 263·86?

3. What is the product of 19 and 20?

4. How many times does 18 go into 150?

5. $21663 \div 10 =$

6. $7200 \div 90 =$

7. Is 8 a factor of 116?

8. Write 23·05 using the 12 hour clock.

9. The Smith family travel 566 km on Wednesday and 976 km on Thursday. How far do they travel altogether?

10. A florist puts 15 daffodils in a bunch. She sells 15 bunches in an hour. How many daffodils is this?

11. $(2^3)^2 + 2^2 =$

12. Does this net make a cube?

13. What is the perimeter of a rectangle measuring 36 cm × 8 cm?

14. Increase £25 by 50%.

15. Two of the angles in a triangle equal 136°. What is the third angle?

Draw 3 different shapes with a perimeter of 22 cm.

(C)

1    $\square \times 6 = 48$

2   46 502, 46 501, 46 500, $\boxed{}$

3    $54 - 38 =$

4    $278 - 159 =$

5    $94 \times 3 =$

6    $53 \div 7 = \square$ r 4

7    $57 + 29 =$

8    $3\frac{2}{5} - \frac{1}{10} =$

9    $5^2 - 3 =$

10   26 124, 26 024, $\boxed{}$, 25 824

11    $-11 + 2 - 8 =$

12    $\frac{8}{14} = \frac{\square}{7}$

13    $(8 \times 6) + 16 =$

14    $33 \div 2 = \square$ r 1

15   70% of 100 =

Copy and complete the Function Machine

× 6

in	out
9	54
12	
34	204
29	
16	
43	258
27	
31	186
46	

(D)

1   Write one thousand and eight point one eight in numerals.

2   3 tenths + 4 tens + 12 thousands + 2 units =

3   Round 44·26 to the nearest whole number.

4    $208 \times 10 =$

5   Continue the pattern: 17, 5, –7, $\boxed{}$, $\boxed{}$

6    $1600 \times 50 =$

7   Is 446 a multiple of 4?

8   What is the volume of a cuboid with sides measuring 4 cm, 5 cm and 3 cm?

9   A bookshop had 5607 books. 700 are detective novels.
How many are not detective novels?

10   The shop has 75 teapots in stock, 15 teapots on each shelf.
How many shelves are used?

11   Complete the ratio, 16:48   1:$\square$

12   I buy 4 sandwiches at £1·35. How much change do I get from £20?

13   What is the area of a shape measuring 17 cm by 4 cm?

14   Children's heights are 1·32 m, 1·34 m, 1·34 m, 1·35 m, 1·31 m, 1·32 m, 1·34 m.
What is the mode?

15   There are 12 coins in a bag. 4 of the coins are silver. What is the probability of not picking a silver coin?

Exercise 19

A

1 $3 \times \boxed{} = 27$

2 $\boxed{}$, 36 400, 36 401, 36 402

3 $42 + 25 + 29 =$

4 $426 + 237 =$

5 $14 \times 8 =$

6 $42 - \boxed{} = 28$

7 $56 \div 6 = 9 \text{ r} \boxed{}$

8 $1\frac{2}{5} + \frac{4}{5} =$

9 $6^3 =$

10 $\boxed{}$, 85 911, 85 923, 85 935

11 $0.4 = \dfrac{\boxed{}}{10} = \boxed{}\%$

12 $-13 + 2 =$

13 $(9 \times 9) - 54 =$

14 $110 \div 6 = 18 \text{ r} \boxed{}$

15 $3.4 + 2.9 =$

Copy and complete.

−	31		3	
	−2			
85		63		
43				27
			61	

B

1 Write 4062·73 in words.

2 What value has the 9 in 364·97?

3 What is the product of 9 and 18?

4 How many times does 12 go into 250?

5 $6713.49 \div 10 =$

6 $5400 \div 90 =$

7 Is 13 a factor of 78?

8 Write 10·25 pm using the 24 hour clock.

9 On sports day team A scored 685 points and team B scored 688 points. How many points did they score altogether?

10 The school magazine has 9 pages. How many pages in 90 copies?

11 $(3^2)^2 + 5 =$

12 Does this net make a cube?

13 What is the perimeter of a rectangle measuring 45 cm × 8 cm?

14 Increase £50 by 10%.

15 Two of the angles in a triangle equal 160°. What is the third angle?

C

1 $\boxed{} \times 8 = 64$

2 $\boxed{}$, 80 999, 80 998, 80 997

3 $93 - 58 =$

4 $627 - 418 =$

5 $37 \times 6 =$

6 $47 \div 5 = \boxed{}$ r 2

7 $37 + 48 =$

8 $1\frac{2}{3} - \frac{1}{6} =$

9 $8^2 - 8 =$

10 60 830, 60 820, 60 810, $\boxed{}$

11 $-18 + 6 - 3 =$

12 $\dfrac{3}{6} = \dfrac{\boxed{}}{2}$

13 $(9 \times 3) + 19 =$

14 $75 \div 4 = \boxed{}$ r 3

15 30% of 110 =

Draw 3 different shapes with an area of 36 cm².

D

1 Write six thousand and fourteen point three eight in numerals.

2 2 units + 4 tenths + 16 thousands + 5 tens =

3 Round 58·19 to the nearest whole number.

4 $327·6 \times 10 =$

5 Continue the pattern:
29, 14, –1, $\boxed{}$, $\boxed{}$

6 $3200 \times 30 =$

7 Is 756 a multiple of 7?

8 What is the volume of a cuboid with sides measuring 8 cm, 2 cm and 3 cm?

9 2730 bulbs are sown in the park.
870 are daffodils.
How many are not daffodils?

10 There are 121 footballers in the competition.
There are 11 players in each team.
How many teams are taking part?

11 Complete the ratio, 13:52   1:$\boxed{}$

12 I hire 4 video tapes at £2·45 each.
How much change do I get from £20?

13 What is the area of a shape measuring 5 cm by 6 cm?

14 Books have the following number of pages:
235, 337, 237, 335, 237. What is the mode?

15 There are 10 pieces of fruit in a bag. 3 pieces are apples.
What is the probability of picking an apple?

Exercise 20

(A)

1. $9 \times \boxed{} = 45$

2. 91 017, 91 018, 91 019, $\boxed{}$

3. $84 + 16 + 14 =$

4. $347 + 409 =$

5. $19 \times 4 =$

6. $96 - \boxed{} = 47$

7. $25 \div 3 = 8 \text{ r } \boxed{}$

8. $\frac{1}{2} + 4\frac{1}{4} =$

9. $7^3 =$

10. 38 459, 38 475, 38 491, $\boxed{}$

11. $0.3 = \dfrac{\boxed{}}{10} = \boxed{}\%$

12. $-19 + 7 =$

13. $(9 \times 4) - 17 =$

14. $149 \div 9 = 16 \text{ r } \boxed{}$

15. $7.3 + 1.8 =$

What are the co-ordinates for this shape?

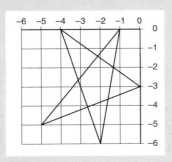

(B)

1. Write 8095·47 in words.

2. What value has the 6 in 235·16?

3. What is the product of 21 and 8?

4. How many times does 31 go into 150?

5. $2769.72 \div 10 =$

6. $8400 \div 70 =$

7. Is 7 a factor of 149?

8. Write 15·15 using the 12 hour clock.

9. Tommy walked 746 m to the shop and then 719 m to his friend's house.
   How far did he walk altogether?

10. If one glass holds 150 ml of lemonade how many ml of lemonade will fill 9 glasses?

11. $(2^3)^3 + 4 =$

12. Does this net make a cube?

13. What is the perimeter of a rectangle measuring 150 cm × 15 cm?

14. Increase £50 by 25%.

15. Two of the angles in a triangle equal 139°. What is the third angle?

C

1. $\boxed{} \times 9 = 45$

2. 31 200, $\boxed{}$, 31 198, 31 197

3. $82 - 67 =$

4. $793 - 329 =$

5. $42 \times 4 =$

6. $45 \div 6 = \boxed{}$ r 3

7. $29 + 43 =$

8. $2\frac{1}{2} - \frac{1}{4} =$

9. $6^2 - 7 =$

10. 37 429, 37 419, 37 409, $\boxed{}$

11. $-16 + 8 - 4 =$

12. $\frac{3}{9} = \frac{\boxed{}}{3}$

13. $(3 \times 6) + 17 =$

14. $74 \div 5 = \boxed{}$ r 4

15. 60% of 60 =

Can you make 179 using + and × and all five numbers only once

3	2	
		34
17		
	42	

D

1. Write eight hundred and four thousand, seven hundred and ninety-three point four nine in numerals.

2. 4 tens + 6 tenths + 3 units + 2 hundreds + 1 hundreth =

3. Round 89·68 to the nearest whole number.

4. $562·7 \times 10 =$

5. Continue the pattern: 49, 24, –1, $\boxed{}$, $\boxed{}$

6. $4900 \times 40 =$

7. Is 637 a multiple of 6?

8. What is the volume of a cuboid with sides measuring 9 cm, 8 cm and 3 cm?

9. Rose has £74·53. She spends £8·95 in the art shop. How much money has she left?

10. There are 105 players in a netball competition. 7 children are in each team. How many teams take part?

11. Complete the ratio, 15:75   1:$\boxed{}$

12. I buy 6 packs of paper cups at 99p each. How much change do I get from £20?

13. What is the area of a shape measuring 18 m by 4 m?

14. Newspapers cost 30p, 35p, 40p, 40p, 45p and 40p. What is the mode?

15. There are 10 pieces of fruit in a bag. 3 pieces are apples. What is the probability of not picking an apple?

Exercise 21

(A)

1. $\Box \times 3 = 21$

2. $134\,278,\ 134\,279,\ \boxed{},\ 134\,281$

3. $74 + 35 + 28 =$

4. $235 + 187 =$

5. $36 \times 4 =$

6. $174 - \Box = 146$

7. $34 \div 5 = \Box\ r\ \Box$

8. $1\frac{1}{6} + 2\frac{1}{2} =$

9. $\sqrt{81} =$

10. $465\,310,\ \boxed{},\ 465\,292,\ 465\,283$

11. $8 - 11 =$

12. $50\% = \dfrac{\Box}{\Box} = 0\cdot\Box$

13. $39 - (3 \times 13) =$

14. $57 \div \Box = 8\ r\ 1$

15. $\frac{3}{5}$ of $70 =$

Draw 3 different shapes with a perimeter of 36 cm.

(B)

1. Write 1033·3 in words.

2. 2·3 < 2·29. True or false?

3. What number is on the bottom of a dice when the 6 is at the top?

4. Double 6 plus 4 then find $\frac{1}{2}$

5. $1055 \div 100 =$

6. If a compass needle moves from North to South in a clockwise direction, how many degrees does it move through?

7. XIX =

8. Approximately how many cm are there in a yard?

9. Jane buys 3 games costing £2·99, £3·99 and £10·99.
   How much does she spend?

10. Mugs are sold in boxes of 15. The café owner buys 4 boxes.
    How many does she get?

11. Two thirds of 18 =

12. Here is a part of a timetable.

	Depart	Arrive
train A	09·35	10·19
train B	09·55	10·45

Which train gets there faster, A or B?

13. What is the perimeter of this shape?

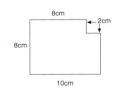

14. Decrease £50 by 50%.

15. Two of the angles in a triangle are 45° and 55°. What is the third angle?

44

C

1. $4 \times \boxed{} = 16$

2. $127\,543, 127\,542, 127\,541, \boxed{}$

3. $24{\cdot}6 \times 10 =$

4. $428 - 139 =$

5. $32 \times 10 =$

6. $86 \div 7 = \boxed{}\ r\ \boxed{}$

7. $29 + \boxed{} = 68$

8. $3\frac{5}{8} - 2\frac{1}{4} =$

9. $2^3 + 4 =$

10. $424\,581, 425\,581, 42\,6581, \boxed{}$

11. $12 - 28 =$

12. $\frac{12}{7} =$

13. $53 + (14 \times 2) =$

14. $65 \div 4 =$

15. $7{\cdot}35 + 2{\cdot}47 =$

Copy and complete the Function Machine
+ 32

in	out
35	
27	59
16	
41	
29	61
32	
10	
46	78
59	

D

1. Write seventeen thousand eight hundred and fifty-seven point nine in numerals.

2. $23 + 48 < 37 + 51$. True or false?

3. Round $17{\cdot}396$ to two decimal places.

4. $0{\cdot}56 \times 100 =$

5. Which is larger, 2^3 of 3^2?

6. Write 16 in roman numerals.

7. Put these numbers in order, largest first: $2{\cdot}14, 4{\cdot}21, 12{\cdot}4$

8. What is the square root of 49?

9. The school library owns 2788 books. This week 1879 books are in the library. How many have been borrowed?

10. How many programmes lasting 24 minutes can fit onto a 240-minute video tape?

11. What is 50% expressed as a ratio?

12. How much change from £20 do I get if I buy 2 books at £3·50 each and a magazine for £1·95?

13. What is the area of this shape?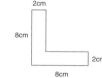

14. What is the mean average of these numbers: 16, 14, 18?

15. If I roll a dice marked from 7–12, what chance do I have of throwing an even number?

Exercise 22

A

1. $\boxed{} \times 4 = 32$

2. 256 498, 256 499, 256 500, $\boxed{}$

3. $35 + 46 + 25 =$

4. $167 + 355 =$

5. $27 \times 9 =$

6. $328 - \boxed{} = 219$

7. $40 \div 6 = \boxed{} \, r \, \boxed{}$

8. $2\frac{1}{2} + 3\frac{1}{4} =$

9. $\sqrt{16} =$

10. 258 392, 258 378, 258 364, $\boxed{}$

11. $7 - 13 =$

12. $75\% = \dfrac{\boxed{}}{\boxed{}} = 0 \cdot \boxed{}$

13. $127 - (4 \times 12) =$

14. $66 \div \boxed{} = 8 \, r \, 2$

15. $\frac{5}{6}$ of $42 =$

Copy and complete.

$\times$	84		60	
$\frac{1}{4}$		18		
			30	
$\frac{3}{4}$				27
	56			

B

1. Write 15 001·9 in words.

2. 2·45 > 2·5. True or false?

3. What is the number on the bottom of a dice when the 3 is at the top?

4. Treble 7 minus 3, then find $\frac{1}{3}$

5. $1878 \div 100 =$

6. A compass needle moves anti-clockwise from South to East. How many degrees does it move through?

7. XXIV = $\boxed{}$

8. Approximately how many kg are there in a lb (pound)?

9. I went on a 3-day journey. I went 421 km, 452 km and 478 km. How far did I travel?

10. Potatoes are planted in rows of 14. The gardener sows 3 rows. How many plants?

11. Three quarters of 40 =

12. Here is a part of a timetable.

	Depart	Arrive
train A	11·57	12.45
train B	12·17	

If train B travels at the same rate as train A, when will it arrive?

13. What is the perimeter of this shape?

10cm · 2cm · 3cm · 6cm · 5cm · 20cm

14. Decrease £25 by 50%.

15. Two of the angles in a triangle are 87° and 48°. What is the third angle?

C

1. $2 \times \boxed{} = 20$

2. 346 540, $\boxed{}$, 346 538, 346 537

3. $3.78 \times 10 =$

4. $342 - 175 =$

5. $44 \times 10 =$

6. $115 \div 8 = \boxed{} \, r \, \boxed{}$

7. $38 + \boxed{} = 73$

8. $4\frac{2}{5} - 3\frac{3}{4} =$

9. $3^3 + 7 =$

10. 378 492, 379 492, $\boxed{}$, 381 492

11. $14 - 27 =$

12. $\frac{15}{8} =$

13. $42 + (13 \times 2) =$

14. $42 \div 3 =$

15. $5.42 + 3.29 =$

Draw 3 different shapes with an area of $12 \, cm^2$.

D

1. Write twenty-nine thousand and eight point four in numerals.

2. $27 + 54 > 38 + 43$. True or false?

3. Round 18·792 to two decimal places.

4. $0.87 \times 100 =$

5. Which is smaller, 4^2 or 33?

6. Write 28 in roman numerals.

7. Put these numbers in order, smallest first: 42, 51·7, 23·9.

8. What is the square root of 81?

9. A factory produces 4876 chocolate bars an hour. 1472 of these are milk chocolate, how many are plain?

10. How many 10-minute appointments can a doctor's receptionist make in 2 hours 25 minutes?

11. What is 25% expressed as a ratio?

12. What change do I get from £20 if I buy 3 sandwiches at 75p each and a can of orange for 50p?

13. What is the area of this shape?

14. What is the mean average of these numbers: 11, 9, 16?

15. There are 24 cubes in a bag. There are 18 green and 6 blue. What is the probability of not pulling out a green cube?

Exercise 23

A

1. $\square \times 7 = 56$

2. 497 375, 497 376, 497 377, $\square$

3. $56 + 37 + 22 =$

4. $529 + 278 =$

5. $66 \times 8 =$

6. $437 - \square = 328$

7. $29 \div 4 = \square\ r\ \square$

8. $4\frac{1}{4} + 2\frac{3}{8} =$

9. $\sqrt{36} =$

10. 558 587, 558 571, 558 555, $\square$

11. $6 - 9 =$

12. $20\% = \dfrac{\square}{\square} = 0\cdot\square$

13. $132 - (15 \times 7) =$

14. $66 \div \square = 9\ r\ 3$

15. $\frac{3}{7}$ of 63 =

What are the co-ordinates for this shape?

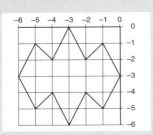

B

1. Write 26 400·2 in words.

2. 2·32 < 2·2. True or false?

3. I throw a dice. It has a 2 on the top. What is the number on the opposite face?

4. Treble 8, plus 6 then find $\frac{1}{5}$

5. $30\cdot75 \div 100 =$

6. If a compass needle moves clockwise from North to South-East, how many degrees does it move through?

7. XXXIV =

8. Approximately how many pints are there in a litre?

9. School A has 561 children. School B has 229 children. School C has 175 children. How many children altogether?

10. There are 4 rows of children in the hall, 13 in each row. How many in total?

11. Four fifths of 25 =

12. Here is a part of a timetable.

	Depart	Arrive
train A	13·27	14·02
train B		15·57

What time does train A leave if both journeys take the same time?

13. What is the perimeter of this shape?

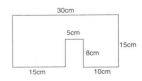

14. Decrease £20 by 25%.

15. Two of the angles in a triangle are 68° and 35°. What is the third angle?

C

1. $3 \times \boxed{} = 21$

2. 609 011, 609 010, $\boxed{}$, 609 008

3. $251 \times 100 =$

4. $217 - 128 =$

5. $28 \times 100 =$

6. $100 \div 6 = \boxed{} \text{ r } \boxed{}$

7. $57 + \boxed{} = 94$

8. $7\frac{2}{7} - 4\frac{3}{5} =$

9. $4^3 + 8 =$

10. 622 407, 621 407, 620 407, $\boxed{}$

11. $17 - 32 =$

12. $\frac{16}{5} =$

13. $29 + (15 \times 3) =$

14. $97 \div 6 =$

15. $2.37 + 1.34 =$

Can you make 1672 using – and × and all five numbers only once

5	4
	21
46	
	37

D

1. Write twenty-six thousand four hundred and one point three in numerals.

2. $63 + 17 < 58 + 29$. True or false?

3. Round 18.149 to two decimal places.

4. $9.26 \times 100 =$

5. Which is larger, 2^3 or 4^2?

6. Write 38 in Roman numerals.

7. Put these numbers in order, largest first: 8.13, 8.3, 8.31

8. What is the cube root of 8?

9. A tea urn holds 2175 ml. Mrs White pours out 1782 ml. How much is left?

10. How many booklets of 4 pages can be made from 94 sheets of paper?

11. What is 20% expressed as a ratio?

12. How much change do I get from £20 if I buy 2 sandwiches at £1.20 each and 2 cakes at 60p each?

13. What is the area of this shape?

6cm, 2cm, 2cm, 2cm, 3cm

14. What is the mean average of these numbers: 12, 18, 18?

15. If I roll a dice marked from 7–12, what chance do I have of throwing a number higher than 8?

Exercise 24

A

1. $\square \times 6 = 42$

2. $\square$, 802 262, 802 263, 802 264

3. $42 + 37 + 29 =$

4. $354 + 459 =$

5. $58 \times 4 =$

6. $235 - \square = 126$

7. $28 \div 3 = \square \, r \, \square$

8. $4\frac{1}{6} + 2\frac{2}{3} =$

9. $\sqrt{25} =$

10. $\square$, 284 008, 283 996, 283 984

11. $14 - 20 =$

12. $10\% = \dfrac{\square}{\square} = 0{\cdot}\square$

13. $143 - (8 \times 16) =$

14. $39 \div \square = 6 \, r \, 3$

15. $\frac{5}{8}$ of $64 =$

Draw 3 different shapes with a perimeter of 40 cm.

B

1. Write 35 480·7 in words.

2. 13·89 > 18·90. True or false?

3. If there is a 1 on the top of a dice, what number is on the opposite face?

4. Double 20 minus 8, then find $\frac{1}{4}$

5. $10786 \div 100 =$

6. If a compass needle moves anti-clockwise from West to North-East, how many degrees does in move through?

7. $XC =$

8. Approximately how many cm are there in an inch?

9. Lorna buys 3 items at £8·50, £2·95 and £3·55.
   How much does she spend?

10. How many eggs in 12 dozen?

11. Seven eighths of 56 =

12. Here is a part of a timetable.

	Depart	Arrive
train A		18·45
train B	18·25	19·15

When does train A leave if both journeys take the same time?

13. What is the perimeter of this shape?

25cm
5cm
20cm
20cm

14. Decrease £20 by 10%.

15. Two of the angles in a triangle are 55° and 38°. What is the third angle?

C

1. $7 \times \boxed{} = 42$

2. $269\,000,\ \boxed{},\ 268\,998,\ 268\,997$

3. $3{\cdot}52 \times 100 =$

4. $576 - 288 =$

5. $48 \times 100 =$

6. $69 \div 4 = \boxed{}\ r\ \boxed{}$

7. $46 + \boxed{} = 82$

8. $2\frac{3}{4} - 1\frac{1}{2} =$

9. $2^3 - 5 =$

10. $219\,584,\ 209\,584,\ \boxed{},\ 189\,584$

11. $15 - 34 =$

12. $\frac{13}{7} =$

13. $37 + (14 \times 3) =$

14. $73 \div 5 =$

15. $5{\cdot}19 + 2{\cdot}45 =$

Copy and complete the
Function Machine
$\times\ 3\ +\ 1$

in	out
6	
12	37
15	
17	
21	
37	
46	139
29	
35	

D

1. Write thirty-five thousand two hundred point six in numerals.

2. $54 - 17 < 45 - 9$. True or false?

3. Round 46·9435 to two decimal places.

4. $33{\cdot}69 \times 100 =$

5. Which is smaller, 3^3 or 4^2?

6. Write 48 in roman numerals.

7. Put these numbers in order, largest first:
3·14, 3·72, 3·8

8. What is the square root of 25?

9. Anne has £28·62 to spend. After her shopping trip she has £11·95 left. How much has she spent?

10. If 108 children join a rounders tournament. They are put into teams of 9. How many teams are there?

11. What is 33% expressed as a ratio?

12. How much change do I get from £20 if I buy 2 notebooks at £1·25 each and 2 pens at £1·75 each?

13. What is the area of this shape?

4cm
2cm
1cm
1cm 1cm
3cm

14. What is the mean average of these numbers: 24, 14, 13?

15. There are 6 bulbs planted in a bowl. They are a mixture of daffodils and tulips. How many different combinations could there be?

Exercise 25

A

1 $\square \times 9 = 27$

2 248 478, 248 479, $\boxed{}$, 248 481

3 $19 + 38 + 73 =$

4 $655 + 365 =$

5 $72 \times 5 =$

6 $153 - \square = 135$

7 $56 \div 6 = \square\ r\ \square$

8 $3\frac{2}{3} + 4\frac{2}{3} =$

9 $\sqrt{49} =$

10 728 206, $\boxed{}$, 728 176, 728 161

11 $9 - 17 =$

12 $25\% = \dfrac{\square}{\square} = 0 \cdot \square$

13 $128 - (14 \times 6) =$

14 $37 \div \square = 7\ r\ 2$

15 $\frac{3}{4}$ of $40 =$

Copy and complete.

%	30		50	
30		12		
	15			
60				54
			37·5	

B

1 Write 87 008·6 in words.

2 $23 \cdot 08 < 23 \cdot 50$. True or false?

3 I throw 2 dice. The numbers on the top are 5 and 3. What are the numbers on the opposite faces?

4 Treble 12, plus 4 then find $\frac{1}{4}$

5 $20932 \div 100 =$

6 If a compass needle moves clockwise from South-East to North-East, how many degrees does it move through?

7 $XL =$

8 Approximately how many grams are there in an ounce?

9 Tom mixes 525 g of flour, 270 g of sugar and 450 g of margarine. What is the total weight of the mixture?

10 The librarian puts 12 new books in each pile. There are 11 piles of new books. How many new books altogether?

11 Five sixths of $30 =$

12 Here is a part of a timetable.

	Depart	Arrive
train A	09·28	10·17
train B	11·53	12·35

Which train is quicker, A or B?

13 What is the perimeter of this shape?

14 Decrease £30 by 20%.

15 Two of the angles in a triangle are 63° and 68°. What is the third angle?

C

1 $8 \times \square = 64$

2 730 531, 730 530, $\boxed{}$, 730 528

3 $302 \times 10 =$

4 $715 - 438 =$

5 $100 \times 33 =$

6 $147 \div 9 = \square \ r \ \square$

7 $27 + \square = 73$

8 $4\frac{3}{15} - 1\frac{1}{5} =$

9 $4^3 - 7 =$

10 540 326, $\boxed{}$, 538 326, 537 326

11 $18 - 29 =$

12 $\frac{17}{9} =$

13 $51 + (13 \times 3) =$

14 $134 \div 9 =$

15 $6\cdot27 + 1\cdot78 =$

Draw 3 different shapes with an area of 18 cm².

D

1 Write forty-seven thousand and forty-nine point one in numerals.

2 $78 - 39 > 68 - 27$ True or false?

3 Round 118·612 to two decimal places.

4 $101\cdot57 \times 100 =$

5 Which is smaller, 2^5 or 3^3?

6 Write 88 in roman numerals.

7 Put these numbers in order, largest first: 2·14, 2·3, 2·12.

8 What is the square root of 64?

9 A shop has 7295 tins of paint. After a week they have 5886 tins left. How many tins have been sold?

10 How many packs of 12 pencils can be made from 150 pencils?

11 What is 10% expressed as a ratio?

12 How much change do I get from £20 if I buy 2 bottles of bubble bath at £1·95 and a soap at 85p?

13 What is the area of the unshaded section?

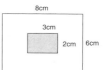

14 What is the mean average of these numbers: 12, 37, 23?

15 There are 18 chocolates in a box. 12 of these are hard centres and 6 are soft centres. What is the probability of not picking a soft centre?

Exercise 26

A

1 $\square \times 3 = 24$

2 $\boxed{}$, 364 065, 364 066, 364 067

3 $84 + 57 + 27 =$

4 $743 + 288 =$

5 $82 \times 2 =$

6 $237 - \boxed{} = 119$

7 $67 \div 8 = \boxed{}\ r\ \boxed{}$

8 $1\frac{1}{5} + 3\frac{2}{10} =$

9 $\sqrt{4} =$

10 $\boxed{}$, 835 497, 835 480, 835 463

11 $10 - 19 =$

12 $1\% = \dfrac{\boxed{}}{\boxed{}} = 0\cdot\boxed{}$

13 $117 - (2 \times 16) =$

14 $86 \div \boxed{} = 9\ r\ 5$

15 $\frac{1}{3}$ of $27 =$

What are the co-ordinates for this shape?

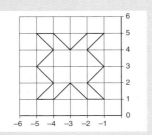

B

1 Write 10 728·69 in words.

2 18·67 > 18·76. True or false?

3 I throw 2 dice. The numbers on the top are 5 and 4. What is the total of the numbers on the opposite faces?

4 Half 48 plus 6, then find $\frac{1}{3}$

5 $2078 \div 100 =$

6 If a compass needle moves anti-clockwise from South-East to South-West, how many degrees does it move through?

7 LXXI =

8 Approximately how many km are there in a mile?

9 In the library, there are 320 picture books, 490 stories, and 495 non-fiction. How many books altogether?

10 There are 12 shelves of videos, 7 to a shelf. How many videos are there?

11 Five ninths of 72 =

12 Here is a part of a timetable.

	Depart	Arrive
train A	16·43	18·06
train B	18·49	20·14

Which train is faster, A or B?

13 What is the perimeter of this shape?

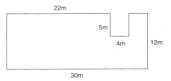

14 Decrease £25 by 20%.

15 Two of the angles in a triangle are 48° and 62°. What is the third angle?

C

1 $9 \times \boxed{} = 63$

2 911 111, $\boxed{}$, 911 109, 911 108

3 $10 \times 5\cdot43 =$

4 $421 - 242 =$

5 $10 \times 63 =$

6 $56 \div 3 = \boxed{} \, r \, \boxed{}$

7 $39 + \boxed{} = 91$

8 $3\frac{3}{5} - 1\frac{1}{3} =$

9 $2^3 + 8 =$

10 $\boxed{}$, 707 906, 697 906, 687 906

11 $20 - 35 =$

12 $\frac{19}{3} =$

13 $27 + (15 \times 2) =$

14 $102 \div 6 =$

15 $3\cdot46 + 1\cdot39 =$

Can you make 214 using +, – and × and all five numbers only once

8   3
        26
27
        31

D

1 Write one hundred and one thousand six hundred and four point two seven in numerals.

2 108 + 67 > 125 + 48. True or false?

3 Round 7·63791 to two decimal places.

4 $37\cdot49 \times 10 =$

5 Which is larger, 7^2 or 2^5?

6 Write 89 in roman numerals.

7 Put these numbers in order, smallest first: 16·52, 12·7, 13·28

8 What is the square root of 16?

9 The first leg of a journey is 2796 km. If the total length of the journey is 5887, how long is the second leg?

10 Glue sticks need to be packed in boxes of 12. How many boxes can be filled from 200 glue sticks?

11 What is 30% expressed as a ratio?

12 How much change do I get from £20 if I buy 2 candlesticks at £3·75 each and 2 candles at 75p each?

13 What is the area of the unshaded section?

14 What is the mean average of these numbers: 25, 16, 25?

15 If I roll a dice marked from 13–18, what chance have I got of scoring less than 16?

Exercise 27

A

1. $\boxed{9} \times 5 = 45$

2. 741 597, 741 598, 741 599, $\boxed{}$

3. $53 + 22 + 48 = 123$

4. $823 + 198 = 1021$

5. $94 \times 6 = 564$

6. $528 - \boxed{219} = 309$

7. $44 \div 7 = \boxed{6}$ r $\boxed{2}$

8. $5\frac{4}{5} + 2\frac{2}{5} = 8\frac{1}{5}$

9. $\sqrt{144} = 12$

10. 178 592, 178 579, 178 566, $\boxed{}$

11. $17 - 21 = -4$

12. $33\% = \dfrac{\boxed{33}}{\boxed{100}} = 0 \cdot \boxed{33}$

13. $78 - (13 \times 4) = 26$

14. $28 \div \boxed{3} = 9$ r 1

15. $\frac{5}{9}$ of 72 = 40

Draw 3 different shapes with a perimeter of 24 cm.

B

1. Write 20 963·62 in words.

2. 108·29 < 108·92. True or false?

3. I throw 2 dice. I score 3 and 6. What is the total of the numbers on the opposite faces?

4. Double 22 plus 6, then find $\frac{1}{5}$

5. $327 \cdot 8 \div 100 =$

6. If a compass needle moves clockwise from South to North-West, how many degrees does it move through?

7. C in roman numerals =

8. Approximately how many feet in a metre?

9. Sarah cuts a long ribbon into three lengths: 228 cm, 498 cm and 627 cm. How long was the original piece of ribbon?

10. There are 14 marbles in each bag. Edward has 5 bags. How many marbles does he have?

11. Seven eighths of 64 =

12. Here is a part of a timetable.

	Depart	Arrive
train A	20·32	21·19
train B	21·08	

If both journeys take the same time, when does train B arrive?

13. What is the perimeter of this shape?

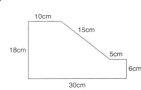

14. Decrease £80 by 25%.

15. Two of the angles in a triangle are 57° and 65°. What is the third angle?

56

C

1. $5 \times \boxed{} = 25$

2. 408 572, 408 571, 408 570, $\boxed{}$

3. $4 \cdot 29 \times 10 =$

4. $605 - 228 =$

5. $69 \times 1000 =$

6. $132 \div 7 = \boxed{} \, r \, \boxed{}$

7. $58 + \boxed{} = 82$

8. $4\frac{1}{4} - 2\frac{1}{2} =$

9. $3^3 - 8 =$

10. 935 242, 835 242, $\boxed{}$, 635 242

11. $13 - 24 =$

12. $\frac{14}{8} =$

13. $33 + (14 \times 2) =$

14. $107 \div 8 =$

15. $3 \cdot 15 + 2 \cdot 48 =$

Copy and complete the Function Machine

$+ \, 5 \times 2$

in	out
16	
21	· 52
9	
14	
27	
31	
48	
34	78
52	

D

1. Write two hundred thousand seven hundred and fifty point seven five in numerals.

2. $5 \times 19 < 4 \times 21$. True or false?

3. Round 10·45297 to two decimal places.

4. $107 \cdot 62 \times 10 =$

5. Which is smaller, 8^2 or 3^3?

6. Write 101 in roman numerals.

7. Put these numbers in order, smallest first: 70·23, 7·2, 7·23

8. What is the cube root of 64?

9. 9753 books have been sorted into fiction and non-fiction. If there are 549 fiction books, how many non-fiction are there?

10. Candles are sold in boxes of 8. How many boxes can be filled from 100 candles?

11. What is $12\frac{1}{2}\%$ expressed as a ratio?

12. How much change do I get from £20 if I buy a CD at £12·99 and a book at £3·50?

13. What is the area of this shape?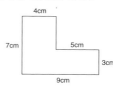

14. What is the mean average of these numbers: 8, 9, 18, 5?

15. I have a mixture of 4 red and blue socks in a bag. How many different combinations might there be?

Exercise 28

A

1. $\boxed{5} \times 8 = 40$

2. 710 638, 710 639, $\boxed{}$, 710 641

3. $28 + 59 + 34 = 121$

4. $638 + 373 = 1011$

5. $46 \times 3 = 138$

6. $625 - \boxed{208} = 417$

7. $38 \div 4 = \boxed{9}\ r\ \boxed{}^{50}$

8. $3\frac{4}{6} + 1\frac{1}{3} = 5$

9. $\sqrt{100} = 10$

10. 349 136, 349 118, $\boxed{}$, 349 082

11. $16 - 24 = -8$

12. $70\% = \dfrac{\boxed{70}}{\boxed{100}} = 0 \cdot \boxed{70}$

13. $90 - (5 \times 16) = 10$

14. $80 \div \boxed{11} = 7\ r\ 3$

15. $\frac{2}{5}$ of $45 = 18$

Copy and complete.

+	32		29	
45		92		
	119			
56	88			104
			102	

B

1. Write 10 808·09 in words.

2. 21·21 > 21·30. True or false?

3. I throw 2 dice and score a 5 and a 1. What is the total of the opposite faces? 8

4. Half 86 plus 7, then find $\frac{1}{3}$ 3̶5̶   16.66

5. $2802 \div 100 = 28.02$

6. If a compass needle moves anti-clockwise from North to North-West, how many degrees does it move through? 45°

7. M in roman numerals = 1000

8. Approximately how many cm are there in a foot? 30

9. Three children playing Canasta scored 585, 602 and 493 points. How many points did they score altogether? 1680

10. Jason fits 14 buns on each baking tray. He fills 4 trays. How many buns does he make? 56

11. Three quarters of 120? 90

12. Here is a part of a timetable.

	Depart	Arrive
train A	13·19	15·07
train B	14·25	16·03

How long does each journey take?

13. What is the perimeter of this shape?

14. Decrease £90 by 10%. £81

15. Two of the angles in a triangle are 36° and 36°. What is the third angle? 108°

C

1   $8 \times \boxed{4} = 32$

2   814 240, $\boxed{}$, 814 238, 814 237

3   $4·07 \times 10 = 40·7$

4   $932 - 547 = 385$

5   $94 \times 10 = 940$

6   $129 \div 8 = \boxed{16}$ r $\boxed{1}$

7   $49 + \boxed{24} = 73$

8   $3\frac{3}{10} - 1\frac{2}{5} = \frac{33}{10} - \frac{14}{10}$
    $= \frac{19}{10} \, 1\frac{9}{10}$

9   $2^3 - 4 = 4$

10 $\boxed{}$, 458 976, 458 876, 458 776

11 $16 - 32 = -16$

12 $\frac{15}{9} = 1\frac{6}{9} = 1\frac{2}{3}$

13 $48 + (12 \times 3) = 84$
    36

14 $51 \div 3 = 13 \; 17$

15 $4·76 + 2·59 =$
    2.59
    7.35

⭐ Draw 3 different shapes with an area of 40 cm².

D

500,001.97

14

1   Write five hundred thousand and one point nine seven in numerals.

2   $108 \div 4 > 110 \div 5$. True or false?
    27        $\cancel{4}22$

3   Round 63·279412 to two decimal places.
    8

4   $101·23 \times 10 =$

5   Which is larger, 10^2 or 3^4?
    100

6   Write 750 in roman numerals.

7   Put these numbers in order, largest first: 103·47, 103·7, 103·4

8   What is the cube root of 16? ?

9   A greengrocer had 9729 apples delivered. 4895 of them are red, the rest are green. How many are green?

10 How many 35 minute programmes will fit onto a 4 hour video tape? 6

11 What is 5% expressed as a ratio? 5:100 1:20

12 How much change from £20 do I get if I buy 2 tubs of luxury ice-cream at £3·49 each and a pizza at £6·25?

13 What is the area of this shape?
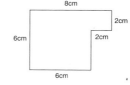

14 What is the mean average of these numbers: 22, 7, 16, 15? 15

15 There are 15 jellies in a bag. 3 are orange flavour, 2 are lime, and the rest are raspberry. What is the probability of picking a raspberry one?

Exercise 29

A

1. $\boxed{3} \times 6 = 18$

2. 582 309, 582 310, $\boxed{}$, 582 312

3. $67 + 43 + 17 = 127$

4. $757 + 264 = 1021$

5. $65 \times 7 = 455$

6. $364 - \boxed{} = 246$ 118

7. $85 \div 9 = \boxed{9} \, r \, \boxed{4}$

8. $4\frac{1}{2} + 2\frac{3}{4} = 7\frac{1}{4}$

9. $\sqrt{64} =$ 8

10. 369 217, 369 201, $\boxed{}$, 369 169

11. $15 - 26 = -11$

12. $3\% = \dfrac{\boxed{3}}{\boxed{100}} = 0.\boxed{03}$

13. $100 - (17 \times 3) = 49$

14. $47 \div \boxed{9} = 5 \, r \, 2$

15. $\frac{2}{3}$ of $24 = 16$

What are the co-ordinates for this shape?

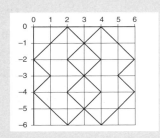

B

1. Write 1273·8 in words.

2. 208·08 > 280·80. True or false?

3. I throw 3 dice. I score 2, 4, 3.   *12*
   What is the total of the opposite faces?

4. Double 18 minus 4, then find $\frac{1}{8}$ *4*

5. $20703 \div 100 =$

6. If a compass needle moves anti-clockwise from East to South-West, how many degrees does it move through?   *225°*

7. MCM in roman numerals =

8. Approximately how many kg are there in a stone?   *6·30*

9. Three farmers have 739, 867, and 496 sheep each. How many sheep is this?   *2·202*

10. There are 15 photographs in each of Hannah's 6 albums.
    How many photographs has she?   *90*

11. Nine tenths of 180.

12. Here is a part of a timetable.

	Depart	Arrive
train A	18·49	20·33
train B		21·03

If both journeys are the same length, when did train B leave?

13. What is the perimeter of this shape?

14. Decrease £1 by 20%.   *80p*

15. Two of the angles in a triangle are 83° and 45°. What is the third angle?   *52°*

60

C

1 $3 \times \boxed{8} = 24$

2   534 455, 534 454, 534 453, $\boxed{}$

3 $100 \times 4.15 =$ 415·0

4 $842 - 574 =$ 268

5 $1000 \times 14 =$ 14000

6 $93 \div 6 = \boxed{15}$ r $\boxed{3}$

7 $37 + \boxed{23} = 60$

8 $6\frac{4}{5} - 3\frac{1}{3} =$ $3\frac{7}{5}$

9 $3^3 + 9 =$ 36

10   192 578, 191 578, 190 578, $\boxed{}$

11 $19 - 37 =$ -18

12 $\frac{18}{6} =$ 3

13 $35 + (12 \times 4) =$ 83

14 $73 \div 4 =$ 18 r 1   18·25   18¼

15 $3.29 + 4.87 =$ 8·16

Can you make 573 using +, − and × and all five numbers only once

4	5
	35
42	
	29

D

1   Write two hundred thousand point eight five in numerals.

2 $24 \times 8 < 28 \times 4$. True or false?

3   Round 78·962791 to two decimal places. 78·96

4 $235.78 \times 10 =$ 2357·8

5   Which is larger, 10^3 or 8^4?   1000 8^4

6   Write 1250 in roman numerals.

7   Put these numbers in order, smallest first: 112·63, 121·36, 113·26

8   What is the square root of 144?   12

9   2798 paintings are hanging in a gallery. 1979 of these have got flowers in them. How many paintings have no flowers on them at all?

10   How many cans of lemonade containing 330 ml can be filled from 2000 ml of lemonade?

11   What is 40% expressed as a ratio?   40 : 100   4 : 10   2 : 5

12   How much change from £20 do I get if I buy a video at £12·49 and 2 blank videos at £1·75 each?

13   What is the area of this shape?

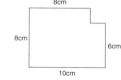

14   What is the mean average of these numbers: 5, 31, 20, 16?

15   There are 24 flowers in a vase. 12 are white, 8 are pink and the rest are yellow. What is the probability of a flower being yellow?

Exercise 30

A

1 $\boxed{} \times 7 = 49$ 7

2 973 208, 973 209, $\boxed{}$, 973 211

3 $97 + 34 + 16 = $ 147

4 $467 + 554 = $ 1021

5 $73 \times 6 = $ 438

6 $692 - \boxed{} = 573$ 119

7 $73 \div 7 = \boxed{} \text{ r } \boxed{}$ 10 r 3

8 $4\frac{1}{4} + 2\frac{1}{4} = $ $6\frac{1}{2}$

9 $\sqrt{1} = $ 1

10 $\boxed{}$, 639 547, 639 531, 639 515

11 $12 - 19 = $ -7

12 $12 \cdot 5\% = \dfrac{\boxed{125}}{\boxed{100}} = 0 \cdot \boxed{125}$

13 $140 - (9 \times 5) = $ 95

14 $146 \div \boxed{24} = 6 \text{ r } 2$ 144

15 $\frac{4}{9}$ of 54 =   24

Draw 3 different shapes with a perimeter of 32 cm.

B

1 Write 10 823·82 in words.

2 161·16 < 116·16. True or false?

3 I throw 3 dice. The dice show 6, 4 and 1. What is my total score for the opposite faces?

4 Treble 13 plus 1, then find $\frac{1}{4}$?

5 $283 \div 100 = $

6 If a compass needle moves clockwise from South-West to East, how many degrees does it move through?

7 MXM in roman numerals =

8 Approximately how many cm are there in a foot?

9 Over three weeks Bernadette saves her pocket money.
She saves £4·97, £8·72 and £10·92.
How much has she managed to save altogether?

10 There are 15 steps in each flight of stairs. Jamie climbs 7 flights.
How many stairs has he climbed?

11 Four fifths of 45?

12 Here is a part of a timetable.

	Depart	Arrive
train A	13·59	15·08
train B		16·37

If both journeys take the same time, when did train B leave?

13 What is the perimeter of this shape?

18cm, 5cm, 7cm, 6cm, 8cm, 6cm

14 Decrease £19 by 10%.

15 Two of the angles in a triangle are 69° and 38°. What is the third angle?

C

1 $7 \times \boxed{} = 49$

2 $\boxed{}$, 400 000, 400 001, 400 002

3 $6.01 \times 100 =$ *601.0*

4 $731 - 642 =$ *89*

5 $51 \times 10 000 =$ *510,000*

6 $175 \div 9 = \boxed{19} \text{ r } \boxed{4}$

7 $59 + \boxed{36} = 95$

8 $6\frac{1}{4} - 2\frac{1}{5} =$ *$6\frac{5}{20} - 2\frac{4}{20}$* *$= 4\frac{1}{5}$*

9 $3^3 - 6 =$ *21*

10 379 024, $\boxed{}$, 378 824, 378 724

11 $11 - 29 =$ *-18*

12 $\frac{12}{9} =$ *$1\frac{1}{3}$*

13 $44 + (16 \times 2) =$ *76*

14 $152 \div 9 =$ *16 r 8*

15 $6.58 + 5.93 =$ *12.51*

Copy and complete the Function Machine
$\div 3 - 2$

in	out
33	
75	23
51	
90	
39	
69	21
102	
63	
87	

D

1 Write seven hundred and nine thousand and nine point one seven in numerals.

2 $369 \div 123 < 492 \div 246$. True or false?

3 Round 107·9696962 to two decimal places.

4 $623471 \times 100 =$

5 Which is smaller, 10^3 or 5^3?

6 Write 1997 in roman numerals.

7 Put these numbers in order, largest first: 4·723, 6·948, 4·8, 6·8

8 What is the cube root of 125?

9 At a soccer match there are 9752 spectators. 5685 are adults. How many are children?

10 How many bunches of 11 flowers can Carole make from 190 flowers?

11 What is 66% expressed as a ratio?

12 How much change do I get from £20 if I buy 2 cinema tickets at £3·50 each and 2 tubs of popcorn at £1·85 each?

13 What is the area of this shape?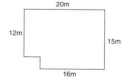

14 What is the mean average of these numbers: 11, 33, 29, 27?

15 There are 30 sweets in a jar. 15 are lemon, 6 are blackcurrant and the rest are lime. What is the probability of picking either a lemon or a lime sweet?